Other Macmillan titles in Electrical and Electronic Engineering

W. A. Atherton, *From Compass to Computer*

B. R. Bannister and D. G. Whitehead, *Fundamentals of Modern Digital Systems*

G. B. Clayton, *Data Converters*

J. C. Cluley, *Electronic Equipment Reliability, second edition*

J. C. Cluley, *Transducers for Microprocessor Systems*

R. F. W. Coates, *Modern Communication Systems, second edition*

Donard de Cogan, *Solid State Devices – A Quantum Physics Approach*

C. W. Davidson, *Transmission Lines for Communication, second edition*

M. E. Goodge, *Analog Electronics*

M. E. Goodge, *Semiconductor Device Technology*

B. A. Gregory, *An Introduction to Electrical Instrumentation and Measurement Systems, second edition*

Paul A. Lynn, *An Introduction to the Analysis and Processing of Signals, third edition*

Paul A. Lynn, *Electronic Signals and Systems*

A. G. Martin and F. W. Stephenson, *Linear Microelectronic Systems*

J. E. Parton, S. J. T. Owen and M. S. Raven, *Applied Electromagnetics, second edition*

Douglas A. Ross, *Optoelectronic Devices and Optical Imaging Techniques*

Trevor J. Terrell, *Introduction to Digital Filters, second edition*

M. J. Usher, *Sensors and Transducers*

L. A. Warnes, *Electronic Materials*

B. W. Williams, *Power Electronics – Devices, Drivers and Applications*

G. Williams, *An Introduction to Electrical Circuit Theory*

Macmillan New Electronics Series
Series Editor: Paul A. Lynn

Rodney F. W. Coates, *Underwater Acoustic Systems*

Paul A. Lynn, *Radar Systems*

A. F. Murray and H. M. Reekie, *Integrated Circuit Design*

Dennis N. Pim, *Television and Teletext*

M. J. N. Sibley, *Optical Communications*

Martin S. Smith, *Introduction to Antennas*

P. M. Taylor, *Robotic Control*

Alan Waters, *Active Filter Design*

Electrical Machines and Drives

An Introduction to Principles and Characteristics

J.D. Edwards

Senior Lecturer
School of Engineering and Applied Sciences
The University of Sussex

MACMILLAN

First edition 1991

Published by
MACMILLAN EDUCATION LTD
Houndmills, Basingstoke, Hampshire RG21 2XS
and London
Companies and representatives
throughout the world

Typeset by
TecSet Ltd, Sutton, Surrey

Printed in Hong Kong

British Library Cataloguing in Publication Data
Edwards, J. D.
Electrical machines and drives: an introduction to
principles and characteristics
1. Electric machinery
I. Title
621.46
ISBN 0-333-53650-9
ISBN 0-333-53651-7 Pbk

Cover photograph courtesy of Printed Motors Limited.

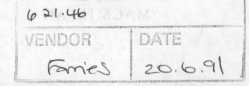

Contents

Preface

This is an extensive revision of the second edition of *Electrical Machines* (Macmillan, 1986), incorporating the latest developments in electrical machines and drive systems. It retains the original aim of its predecessor: to give a short modern account of the principles of electrical machines and drives in a form accessible to the non-specialist, yet with sufficient rigour to provide a basis for more advanced studies. The first six chapters are unchanged in scope; they cover fundamental principles and the 'classical' electrical machines: DC commutator machines, AC synchronous machines and AC induction machines. The introduction to generalised machine theory has been removed, since it no longer seems appropriate in a text at this level. In its place are four new chapters on DC and AC drive systems.

Many applications of electrical machines require an adjustable speed. In the past this has been achieved with ingenious machines such as the AC commutator motors, or with constant-speed motors and mechanical variable-speed transmissions. These machines have been superseded by combinations of power electronic controllers and electrical machines which form the modern drive system. Chapters 7 and 8 cover the principles of power electronic controllers as applied to the classical AC and DC machines. Chapters 9 and 10 cover the newer non-classical machines which work in conjunction with special-purpose electronic controllers: stepper motors, electronically commutated (or brushless) DC machines, and switched reluctance motors.

A distinctive feature of the earler book has been retained: a unified treatment of AC and DC machines based on the interaction of currents and magnetic fields, which gives a clear physical picture of the operating principles. The treatment is fully quantitative, and meets the requirements of rigour and simplicity by taking the simplest model of a machine which will demonstrate the essential features of its operation. Departures from the ideal are mentioned only briefly, since these form the subject of specialised study.

AC machines generally give students the most difficulty; a feature of this book is a novel approach to AC machines, introduced in chapter 4 and developed in chapters 5 and 6. Traditionally, the concepts of MMF and flux dominate the theory; these are useful concepts, but they make the action of the machine difficult to visualise because they are one step removed from the fundamental current and field. I have therefore based the theory on the concepts of current density and flux density. These concepts give an immediate picture of the electromagnetic action; they also lead directly to the rotating field principle, the torque equation and the equivalent circuit.

ix

The reader is assumed to have an elementary knowledge of electromagnetism, circuit theory, and vectors. Background material is listed in the Bibliography at the end of the book. Space has limited the number of worked examples and problems for solution. In general the problems at the ends of the chapters are not straightforward, and they extend the material of the chapter. Readers who require more problems and worked examples will find them in the books listed in the Bibliography.

I wish to thank the Controller of Her Majesty's Stationery Office and the Longman Group for permission to reproduce figures 1.36 and 2.12 respectively, and several manufacturers, acknowledged in the text, for photographs of machines. I am grateful to reviewers and my university colleagues for suggestions; to second-year engineering students for encouraging me to find better ways of presenting machine theory; and to my wife for many hours of work with the computer in preparing both text and drawings.

J. D. Edwards

Notation, Units and Symbols

SI units are used throughout the book, and the recommendations of the British Standards Institution [1] are followed for unit names and symbols. With electrical quantities, the usual convention is followed in denoting time-varying values by lower-case symbols and steady values or magnitudes by upper-case symbols. Three kinds of vector quantity occur in the book: space phasors, time phasors and three-dimensional vectors. Bold-face type is used for all these quantities, in line with normal practice, for example I, B. In some cases the same symbol may be used for a field vector or a space phasor; the context will always show which meaning is intended.

In general the recommendations of the Institution of Electrical Engineers[2] and the British Standards Institution [3] have been followed for symbols, abbreviations and subscripts. One exception is the symbol for linear current density; the recommended symbol A seems a poor choice because it is the established symbol for magnetic vector potential, and distinct symbols for both quantities are needed in advanced work. The symbol chosen is K, which follows Stratton [4] and some current practice.

There is one area of notation in which no uniformity exists: the choice of symbols for the infinitesimal elements in line, surface and volume integrals. After careful consideration the notation adopted is that of Stratton [4], in which ds, da and dv denote the elements of path length, area and volume respectively. This is a consistent and convenient notation; it justifies the use of the subscript s for the tangential component of a vector; it releases capital letters for designating finite regions or quantities; and there is no confusion in advanced work between the symbols for length or area and the Poynting vector S or the vector potential A.

The following lists refer only to the usage in this book. Further information will be found in the references already cited and in Massey [5].

List of principal symbols

Symbol	Quantity	Unit	Unit symbol
A	area	square metre	m^2
a	radius	metre	m
B, B	magnetic flux density	tesla	T
B	flux density phasor	tesla	T
C	capacitance	farad	F
da, da	element of area	square metre	m^2
ds, ds	element of path length	metre	m
dv	element of volume	cubic metre	m^3
E, E	electric field strength	volt/metre	V/m
$E; E$	excitation voltage phasor; RMS magnitude	volt	V
$E; E$	induced EMF phasor; RMS magnitude	volt	V
E, e	electromotive force	volt	V
F, F	mechanical force	newton	N
F	magnetomotive force	ampere	A
F_x	x component of force	newton	N
f, f	force per unit volume	newton/metre^3	N/m^3
f	frequency	hertz	Hz
g	airgap length	metre	m
H, H	magnetising force	ampere/metre	A/m
$I; I$	current phasor; RMS magnitude	ampere	A
I_0	no-load current	ampere	A
I_{01}	loss component of I_0	ampere	A

I_{0m}	magnetising component of I_0	ampere	A
I, i	current	ampere	A
J, J	current density	ampere/metre^2	A/m^2
J	moment of inertia	kilogram metre^2	kg m^2
j	$\pi/2$ operator, $\sqrt{(-1)}$	–	–
K, K	linear current density	ampere/metre	A/m
K	current density phasor	ampere/metre	A/m
K	DC machine constant	{ volt second/weber radian	V s/Wb rad
		newton metre/ampere^2	N m/A^2
K_a	armature constant	{ volt second/ampere radian	V s/A rad
		newton metre/weber ampere	N m/Wb A
K_f	field constant	weber/ampere	Wb/A
k	torque constant	newton metre/tesla^2	N m/T^2
L	self-inductance	henry	H
L_m	magnetising inductance	henry	H
l	leakage inductance	henry	H
l	length	metre	m
M	mutual inductance	henry	H
m	number of phases	–	–
N	number of turns	–	–
n	Steinmetz index	–	–
n	turns ratio	–	–
P	power	watt	W
P_e	electrical power	watt	W
P_m	mechanical power	watt	W
p	d/dt operator	1/second	1/s
p	number of pole pairs	–	–

Symbol	Quantity	Unit	Unit symbol
p_e	eddy current power loss per unit volume	watt/metre^3	W/m^3
p_h	hysteresis power loss per unit volume	watt/metre^3	W/m^3
q	electric charge	coulomb	C
R	resistance	ohm	Ω
R_e	equivalent total resistance	ohm	Ω
R_c	core loss resistance	ohm	Ω
r	radius	metre	m
S	reluctance	ampere/weber	A/Wb
s	fractional slip	—	—
T	torque	newton metre	N m
T_m	mechanical output torque	newton metre	N m
T_θ	torque associated with angle θ	newton metre	N m
t, t	stress	newton/metre^2	N/m^2
t	time	second	s
U	magnetic potential difference	ampere	A
u, u	linear velocity	metre/second	m/s
$V; V$	voltage phasor; RMS magnitude	volt	V
V, v	terminal voltage, electric potential difference	volt	V
W	energy, work done	joule	J
W_e	electrical energy	joule	J
w_h	hysteresis energy loss per unit volume	joule/metre^3	J/m^3

W_m	magnetic stored energy	joule	J
X	reactance	ohm	Ω
X_e	equivalent total reactance	ohm	Ω
X_m	mutual or magnetising reactance	ohm	Ω
X_s	synchronous reactance	ohm	Ω
x	leakage reactance	ohm	Ω
Z, Z	impedance	ohm	Ω
Z	maximum linear conductor density	1/metre	1/m
α, β, γ	general angles	radian	rad
δ	load angle, angle between		
	magnetic field axes	radian	rad
δ	depth of penetration	metre	m
ϵ	voltage regulation	–	–
η	efficiency	–	–
θ	angular displacement, rotor angle	radian	rad
Λ	permeance	weber/ampere	Wb/A
λ_h	Steinmetz coefficient	–	–
μ	absolute permeability $= \mu_0 \mu_r$	henry/metre	H/m
μ_0	magnetic constant $= 4\pi \times 10^{-7}$	henry/metre	H/m
μ_r	relative permeability	–	–
ρ	charge per unit volume	coulomb/metre^3	C/m^3
ρ	resistivity $= 1/\sigma$	ohm metre	Ω m
σ	conductivity $= 1/\rho$	siemens/metre	S/m
τ	time constant	second	s
τ_{em}	electromechanical time constant	second	s

Symbol	Quantity	Unit	Unit symbol
Φ	magnetic flux phasor	weber	Wb
Φ	magnetic flux, flux per pole	weber	Wb
Φ_l	leakage flux	weber	Wb
ϕ	phase angle, angular displacement	radian	rad
ψ	angular displacement	radian	rad
Ω, ω	angular velocity	radian/second	rad/s
ω	angular frequency $= 2\pi f$	radian/second	rad/s
ω_r	rotor angular velocity	radian/second	rad/s
ω_s	synchronous angular velocity	radian/second	rad/s

General subscripts

a	armature
av	average
f	field
m, max	maximum value
n	normal component
r	radial component
s	tangential component
1, 2	primary, secondary; stator, rotor
α, β	two-phase quantities
a, b, c	three-phase quantities

Decimal prefixes

10^6	mega	M
10^3	kilo	k
10^{-2}	centi	c
10^{-3}	milli	m
10^{-6}	micro	μ

Abbreviations

AC	alternating current
DC	direct current
EMF	electromotive force
MMF	magnetomotive force
rev/min	revolutions per minute
rev/s	revolutions per second
RMS	root-mean-square

References

1 BS 3763, *The International System of Units (SI)* (London: British Standards Institution, 1976).
2 IEE, *Symbols and Abbreviations for Electrical and Electronic Engineering*, 3rd ed. (London: Institution of Electrical Engineers, 1980).
3 BS 5775, *Specification for Quantities, Units and Symbols* (London: British Standards Institution, 1982).
4 J. A. Stratton, *Electromagnetic Theory* (New York: McGraw-Hill, 1941).
5 B. S. Massey, *Units, Dimensional Analysis and Physical Similarity* (London: Van Nostrand Reinhold, 1971).

1 General Principles

1.1 Introduction

In 1820 Oersted discovered the magnetic effect of an electric current, and the first primitive electric motor was built in the following year. Faraday's discovery of electromagnetic induction in 1831 completed the foundations of electromagnetism, and the principles were vigorously exploited in the rapidly growing field of electrical engineering [1]. By 1890 the main types of rotating electrical machine had been invented, and the next forty years saw the development of many ingenious variations, along with refinement of the basic types. This was the golden age of machine development; electronics was in its infancy, and the rotating machine was king. Many machines are now obsolete which were once made in large numbers. Thus the cross-field DC machines, or rotary amplifiers, have been replaced by solid-state power amplifiers; while the Schrage motor and other ingenious variable-speed AC machines have given way to the thyristor-controlled DC motor and the inverter-fed induction motor.

Electrical machines may be broadly divided into two groups. The first group comprises the three types of classical machine which were invented in the nineteenth century: simple DC machines, AC synchronous machines and AC induction machines. In the second group are the so-called non-classical machines which are of much more recent origin: stepper motors, brushless DC motors and switched reluctance motors. The distinctive feature of the non-classical machines is their dependence on power electronic circuits to control the currents in the active coils; their development was made possible by advances in semi-conductor technology. Stepper motors are complementary to the classical machines because they are designed for motion in discrete steps rather than continuous rotation. Brushless DC motors and switched reluctance motors, on the other hand, are designed for continuous rotation; they are in direct competition with classical machines and are beginning to displace them in some applications.

Classical machines still dominate the world of electrical machines and drives. Most of the motive power for industry is supplied by induction motors operating directly from the AC mains as constant-speed drives. There are many applications, however, which require an adjustable-speed drive; this can be achieved by power electronic control of a classical machine. The dominance of the classical

1

machines, and the extension of their domain through the use of power electronics, is reflected in the structure of this book.

As might be expected from their historical development, the classical machines share a common physical basis for their operation. This permits a progressive development of the subject from the general principles outlined in this chapter, beginning with the effects discovered by Oersted and Faraday. These two effects and their interrelation are seen most clearly when a current-carrying conductor is free to move in a magnetic field of constant intensity; this case is considered in section 1.2. But in most practical machines the conductors are not free to move; they are embedded in slots in the iron core of the machine, and forces act on the iron as well as on the conductors. It is necessary therefore to consider force production and EMF generation in more general terms, which is done in sections 1.3 and 1.4. Magnetic materials form an essential part of electrical machines; some of their properties are discussed in section 1.5, and the important concept of the magnetic circuit is introduced in section 1.6.

1.2 Conductor moving in a magnetic field

When a conductor moves in a magnetic field, an EMF is generated; when it carries a current in a magnetic field, a force is produced. Both of these effects may be deduced from one of the most fundamental principles of electromagnetism, and they provide the basis for a number of devices in which conductors move freely in a magnetic field. It has already been mentioned that most electrical machines employ a different form of construction, and the concepts developed in the next two sections are necessary for a proper understanding of their operation. Nevertheless the equations developed in this section for the force and the induced EMF remain valid for many practical machines; this important and useful result will be justified in chapter 2.

Induced EMF in a moving conductor

Consider a conductor moving with a velocity denoted by the vector u in a magnetic field B (figure 1.1). If the conductor slides along wires connected to a voltmeter, there will be a reading on the meter, showing that an EMF is being generated in the circuit. The effect may be explained in terms of the Lorentz equation for the force on a moving charge q

$$F = q(E + u \times B) \quad \text{newtons} \qquad (1.1)$$

where q is the charge in coulombs, E the electric field strength in volts/metre, u the velocity in metres/second, and B the magnetic flux density in teslas. If the conductor is initially at rest, there will be no electric field E and no reading on

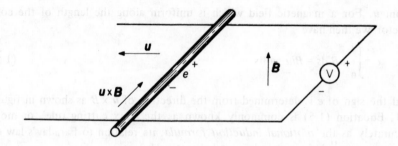

Figure 1.1 Moving conductor: induced EMF

the voltmeter. When the conductor is moving with velocity u, a force $qu \times B$ will act on any charged particle within the conductor, and the free charges (conduction electrons) will begin to move under the action of the force. There will be an accumulation of negative charge at one end of the conductor, leaving a surplus of positive charge at the other end; this will set up an electrostatic field E, and charge separation will continue until the force qE is exactly equal and opposite to $qu \times B$. The net force is then zero; there is no further motion of charge, and we have

$$E = -u \times B \qquad (1.2)$$

The quantity $u \times B$ may be regarded as an induced electric field produced by the motion of the conductor, and this is opposed by an equal and opposite electrostatic field E produced by a distribution of electric charge. In virtue of the electrostatic field E there will be an electrostatic potential difference between the ends of the conductor given by the line integral of E along any path joining the ends PQ

$$v = -\int_{P}^{Q} E \cdot ds \text{ volts} \qquad (1.3)$$

and this will be measured by a voltmeter connected between the wires. From eqn (1.2) this may be written as $v = e$, where

$$e = \int_{P}^{Q} u \times B \cdot ds \text{ volts} \qquad (1.4)$$

and e may be regarded as the EMF induced in the conductor by its motion in the magnetic field. The integral may conveniently be taken along the axis of the conductor, which is a line of length l denoted by the vector l = PQ. If u, B and l are mutually perpendicular, the induced electric field $u \times B$ will be parallel to l, and its direction is determined by the right-hand screw rule of the vector product: if you look in the direction of $u \times B$, then B is displaced clockwise from u. For a magnetic field which is uniform along the length of the conductor, we then have

$$e = \int_0^l uB \, ds = Blu \text{ volts} \tag{1.5}$$

and the sign of e is determined from the direction of $u \times B$ as shown in figure 1.1. Equation (1.5) is commonly known as the 'flux cutting rule', or more accurately as the *motional induction formula*; its relation to Faraday's law of electromagnetic induction is discussed in section 1.3.

Conductor resistance

Suppose that a resistor is connected in place of the voltmeter, so that a current i flows. If this current is distributed uniformly over the cross-section of the conductor, and the cross-sectional area is A, the magnitude of the current density is

$$J = \frac{i}{A} \text{ amperes/metre}^2 \tag{1.6}$$

and its direction is along the conductor, as shown in figure 1.2. Since the total force acting on unit charge is $E + u \times B$, Ohm's law for the moving conductor is

$$J = \sigma(E + u \times B) \tag{1.7}$$

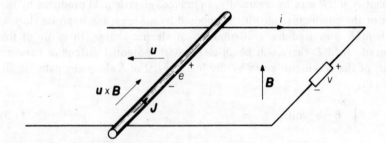

Figure 1.2 Moving conductor: induced current

where σ is the conductivity of the material. Thus the electrostatic field E must be slightly less than the induced electric field $u \times B$ when a current is flowing, the resultant force per unit charge being just sufficient to maintain the flow of current. The potential difference between the ends of the conductor is now given by

$$v = -\int E \cdot ds = \int u \times B \cdot ds - \int \frac{1}{\sigma} J \cdot ds$$

$$= \int_0^l uB \, ds - \int_0^l \frac{i}{\sigma A} \, ds = Blu - \frac{li}{\sigma A} \tag{1.8}$$

or

$$v = e - Ri \tag{1.9}$$

where $e = Blu$ is the induced EMF in volts and $R = l/\sigma A$ is the resistance of the conductor in ohms. The system may be represented by an equivalent circuit, as shown in figure 1.3.

Electromagnetic force on a conductor

Take the same configuration of a conductor in a magnetic field, and suppose initially that the conductor is stationary (figure 1.4). If a current i is flowing,

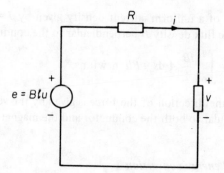

Figure 1.3   Equivalent circuit for a moving conductor

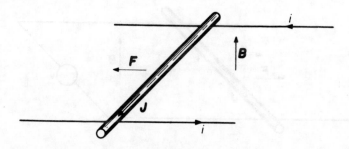

Figure 1.4   Force on a current-carrying conductor

there will be a flow of free charge along the conductor; let ρ be the charge per unit volume, and U the average drift velocity of the charge. This moving charge will experience a force in a magnetic field, and from eqn (1.1) the force per unit volume is

$$f = \rho U \times B \ \ \text{newtons/metre}^3 \tag{1.10}$$

Since the free charge cannot escape from the sides, this force is transmitted to the conductor. We may express the force in terms of the current by noting that the current density J is given by

$$J = \rho U \tag{1.11}$$

The force per unit volume is therefore

$$f = J \times B \tag{1.12}$$

and the total force on the conductor is given by the volume integral

$$F = \int J \times B \ dv \ \ \text{newtons} \tag{1.13}$$

In the simple case of a uniform current density given by $J = i/A$ (eqn 1.6), and a uniform magnetic flux density B perpendicular to the conductor

$$F = \int JB \ dv = \int_0^l \frac{iB}{A} A \ ds = Bli \ \ \text{newtons} \tag{1.14}$$

From eqn (1.12) the direction of the force is given by the vector product $J \times B$, and it is perpendicular to both the conductor and the magnetic field.

Electromechanical energy conversion

Figure 1.5 shows the conductor connected to a voltage source v. There is a current i flowing, and the conductor is moving with a velocity u. The directions

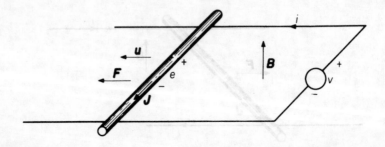

Figure 1.5 Moving current–carrying conductor

of the force F and the induced EMF e are shown in the figure. Since the force F and the velocity u are in the same direction. the conductor does mechanical work at the rate

$$P_m = F \cdot u = Fu \text{ watts} \tag{1.15}$$

The voltage source v is driving a current i into the circuit, and it therefore does work at the rate

$$P_e = vi \text{ watts} \tag{1.16}$$

Since the direction of current flow is the reverse of that in figure 1.2, eqn (1.9) becomes

$$v = e + Ri$$
$$= Blu + Ri \tag{1.17}$$

and we also have the force equation

$$F = Bli \tag{1.14}$$

Multiplying eqn (1.17) by i and eqn (1.14) by u gives

$$P_e = vi = Blui + Ri^2$$
$$P_m = Fu = Bliu$$

It follows that

$$P_e = P_m + Ri^2 \tag{1.18}$$

showing that the electrical input power P_e is equal to the mechanical output power P_m plus the ohmic losses in the conductors; the device is acting as a motor, converting electrical energy into mechanical energy. For the current to flow in the direction shown, the applied voltage v must exceed the induced EMF e; if v is smaller than e the direction of current flow is reversed, and the direction of the force F is reversed in consequence. The conductor then absorbs mechanical energy at the rate $P_m = Fu$; the voltage source likewise absorbs electrical energy at the rate $P_e = vi$, and

$$P_m = P_e + Ri^2 \tag{1.19}$$

The device is acting as a generator, converting mechanical energy into electrical energy plus ohmic losses. Thus the process of energy conversion is reversible, and there is no fundamental difference between generator and motor action.

Applications

Among the best-known applications of the conductor in a magnetic field are the moving-coil loudspeaker (figure 1.6) and the moving-coil meter (figure 1.7). In each of these devices the conductor, in the form of a coil, moves in the uniform radial field of a permanent magnet; motion of the coil is opposed by a spring, giving a displacement proportional to the coil current. The direct proportionality of the force or displacement to the current makes the moving-coil principle particularly useful for instrumentation. In the force-balance accelerometer, for instance, a feedback system senses the coil displacement and adjusts the current until the electromagnetic force exactly balances the acceleration reaction force. The coil current then gives a measure of the acceleration precise enough for modern inertial navigation techniques.

Another application is a special type of electrical machine. Most conventional motors and generators depend for their operation on the force between magnetised iron parts; but in the homopolar machine the force is developed directly on a conductor moving in a magnetic field of constant intensity. Faraday in 1831 made the first generator using this principle, in the form of a circular disc rotating in a magnetic field (figure 1.8). Each element of the disc at a radial distance r from the axis is moving with velocity $u = \omega r$ perpendicular to the magnetic field. The induced electric field $\boldsymbol{u} \times \boldsymbol{B}$ is directed along the radius, so there will be an

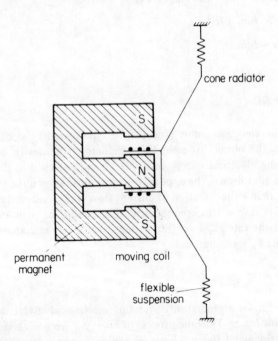

Figure 1.6 Moving–coil loudspeaker

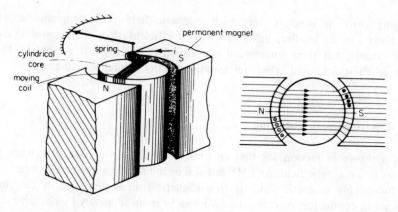

Figure 1.7 Moving-coil meter

EMF induced between the centre of the disc and the periphery. Integration along a path such as PQ gives

$$e = \int_P^Q u \times B \cdot ds = \int_0^a B\omega r\, dr = \tfrac{1}{2}B\omega a^2 \quad \text{volts} \tag{1.20}$$

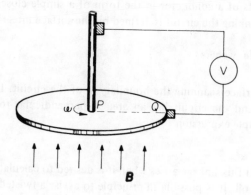

Figure 1.8 Faraday disc generator

where a is the radius of the disc in metres and ω the angular velocity in radians/second. The generated voltage is rather low for small machines at normal speeds, if the flux density is limited (as it usually is) by the saturation of iron to about 2 teslas. For example, if $a = 100$ mm, $\omega = 100$ rad/s (≈ 1000 rev/min) and $B = 2$ T, then $e = 1$ V. Large machines have been built for special low-voltage heavy-current applications, and an interesting development is the use of superconducting coils to generate very high magnetic fields [2]. Superconducting machines can be smaller, lighter and more efficient than their conventional counterparts, but their commercial application is restricted at present by the poor reliability of liquid helium refrigerators for the superconducting coils.

1.3 Electromagnetic induction

It was shown in section 1.2 that an EMF is induced in a conductor when it moves in a magnetic field. An EMF can also be induced in a stationary circuit by a time-varying magnetic field. If this magnetic field is produced by currents flowing in conductors or coils, the EMF can be induced merely by changing the current; no motion of any part of the system is required. The effect is termed transformer induction, and it appears to be physically quite distinct from motional induction. Both effects are included in Faraday's law of electromagnetic induction, which relates the induced EMF in a circuit to the rate of change of the magnetic flux linking the circuit.

Flux linkage

If a circuit consists of a conductor in the form of a simple closed curve C, the magnetic flux Φ linking the circuit is defined by the surface integral

$$\Phi = \int_S B \cdot da \text{ webers} \tag{1.21}$$

where S is any surface spanning the boundary C of the circuit. If the magnetic field is uniform and the circuit has an area A perpendicular to the field, this reduces to the simple expression

$$\Phi = BA \tag{1.22}$$

The concept of flux linkage arises when it is desired to calculate the flux linking a multi-turn coil. It is possible in principle to devise a twisted surface resembling an Archimedian screw, bounded by the turns of the coil, and to evaluate the integral in eqn (1.21) over this surface. But it is simpler to suppose that each turn links a certain amount of flux, so that the total flux linking the coil is the sum of the contributions from the individual turns. Thus if each turn links a flux Φ and the coil has N turns, then the total flux linking the coil, or flux linkage, is given by

$$\psi = N\Phi \text{ webers} \tag{1.23}$$

If the magnetic field is uniform and parallel to the axis of the coil, and each turn has an area A, then

$$\psi = NBA \qquad (1.24)$$

Usually the field is not uniform and the flux through an individual turn will depend on its position (figure 1.9). The total flux linking the coil is then given by the sum

$$\psi = \sum_{r=1}^{N} \Phi_r \text{ webers} \qquad (1.25)$$

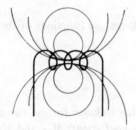

Figure 1.9   Flux linkage: non–uniform field

and an average flux per turn may be defined by the relation

$$\Phi_{av} = \psi/N \qquad (1.26)$$

Inductance

If permanent magnets are excluded, the flux linking a coil will depend on (a) the current flowing in the coil and (b) currents flowing in any adjacent coils or conductors.

Self-inductance

With a single coil carrying a current i we have

$$\psi = f(i) \qquad (1.27)$$

When there are no ferromagnetic materials present (the coil is air-cored) the relationship is linear; thus

$$\psi = Li \qquad (1.28)$$

where L is a constant known as the *self-inductance* of the coil. The unit of L is the henry when ψ is in webers and i in amperes. When the coil has an iron core the relationship between ψ and i is no longer linear, on account of the magnetic properties of the iron. The form of eqn (1.28) may still be used, but the coefficient L is no longer a constant; this can be made explicit by writing

$$\psi = iL(i) \tag{1.29}$$

In order to simplify the analysis it is often assumed that the inductance of an iron-cored coil is a constant; this assumption must be used with caution, for it can sometimes give completely erroneous results. This point will be discussed more fully in section 1.6.

Mutual inductance

With two coils the flux linkages are functions of the coil currents and the geometry of the system. Thus

$$\psi_1 = L_1 i_1 + M_{12} i_2$$
$$\psi_2 = L_2 i_2 + M_{21} i_1 \tag{1.30}$$

where ψ_1 and ψ_2 are the flux linkages for the two coils, and i_1 and i_2 are the corresponding currents. The coefficients M_{12} and M_{21} are known as the *mutual inductances*. When the coils do not have iron cores, it may be shown [3] that the mutual inductance coefficients are constant and equal, that is

$$M_{12} = M_{21} = M \tag{1.31}$$

If ψ_{12} is the flux linking the first coil due to a current i_2 in the second, and ψ_{21} is the flux linking the second coil due to a current i_1 in the first, then the mutual inductance is given by

$$M = \frac{\psi_{12}}{i_2} = \frac{\psi_{21}}{i_1} \tag{1.32}$$

This reciprocal property is particularly useful when the mutual inductance has to be measured or calculated, for one of the two alternative expressions in eqn (1.32) is often easier to evaluate than the other.

Faraday's law

Faraday's law of electromagnetic induction states that the EMF induced in a circuit is proportional to the rate of change of flux linkages. In SI units the constant of proportionality is unity, so that

$$e = \pm \frac{d\psi}{dt} \text{ volts} \tag{1.33}$$

The question of the sign in eqn (1.33) sometimes causes difficulty. Traditionally a negative sign is used in deference to Lenz's law, which states that any current produced by the EMF tends to oppose the flux change. But this is inconsistent with the definition of inductance given in eqn (1.28) and the usual circuit conventions shown in figure 1.10. If we take the positive sign in eqn (1.33) and substitute for ψ from eqn (1.28), then

$$e = +L \frac{di}{dt} \tag{1.34}$$

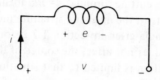

Figure 1.10   Induced EMF in a coil

For a pure inductance, with no internal resistance, Kirchhoff's voltage law applied to the circuit gives

$$v - e = 0$$

so that

$$v = e \tag{1.35}$$

Consequently the terminal voltage v is given by

$$v = +L \frac{di}{dt} \tag{1.36}$$

and this is the equation which defines the inductance element in circuit theory. The correct form of Faraday's law is therefore

$$e = +\frac{d\psi}{dt} \tag{1.37}$$

and Lenz's law may be used to resolve any uncertainty about the positive directions of e and ψ in the circuit.

Calculation of the induced EMF

Faraday's law relates the induced EMF to the rate of change of flux linkage, regardless of the way in which the change occurs. The flux linkage of a circuit may be changed in several ways: the strength of the magnetic field may be altered, either by moving the circuit relative to the source of the field or by varying the currents which create the field, or the boundary of the circuit may be deformed while the magnetic field remains unchanged. The moving conductor in section 1.2 is an example of this last case. Consider the circuit formed by the voltmeter, the fixed rails, and the moving conductor; the area of this circuit increases steadily, and the rate of change of flux is equal to *Blu*. This result agrees with the previous calculation. In all cases the induced EMF may be calculated by the direct application of Faraday's law, and this is the only satisfactory method when motional and transformer effects are both present.

Particular care is needed when calculating the EMF in a moving conductor. It is tempting to use the 'flux cutting formula' *e = Blu* in all cases, but this can give incorrect results when parts of the magnetic structure move with the conductor. The derivation of the formula given in section 1.2 is for the particular case of a conductor whose motion does not affect the source of the magnetic field in any way, and its direct application is limited to that situation. More complex problems can be treated by expressing the total magnetic field as the sum of components from different parts of the magnetic structure, and taking the sum of *Blu* terms with the appropriate values of *u* [4]. But the direct application of Faraday's law is the safest procedure in this kind of problem. Carter [3] gives a particularly good discussion of electromagnetic induction and some apparent paradoxes.

Induced EMF and inductance

The self-inductance and mutual-inductance coefficients can often be changed by relative movement of parts of the system, and Faraday's law gives the correct value for the induced EMF in these cases. For example, with the single coil shown in figure 1.10 the induced EMF is given by

$$e = \frac{\mathrm{d}\psi}{\mathrm{d}t} = \frac{\mathrm{d}}{\mathrm{d}t}(Li) = L\frac{\mathrm{d}i}{\mathrm{d}t} + i\frac{\mathrm{d}L}{\mathrm{d}t} \qquad (1.38)$$

Thus if the motion of a part of the system causes L to change, there will be an EMF term additional to the normal EMF of self-induction. The voltage equation for the circuit should therefore be written as

$$v = Ri + \frac{\mathrm{d}}{\mathrm{d}t}(Li) \qquad (1.39)$$

Similarly, with the coupled coils shown in figure 1.11 the voltage equations are

$$v_1 = R_1 i_1 + \frac{\mathrm{d}}{\mathrm{d}t}(L_1 i_1 + M i_2)$$

$$\qquad (1.40)$$

$$v_2 = R_2 i_2 + \frac{\mathrm{d}}{\mathrm{d}t}(L_2 i_2 + M i_1)$$

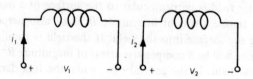

i_1 V_1 i_2 V_2

Figure 1.11   Coupled coils

When there is no motion of parts of the system the inductance coefficients are constant, and these equations reduce to the ordinary equations of coupled circuit theory.

1.4 Electromagnetic forces

In section 1.2 a method was given for calculating the force on a conductor in a magnetic field. In many practical devices, including rotating machines, magnetic forces act on the iron parts as well as on the conductors. These forces on the magnetised iron parts are often the dominant ones, and there is a need to calculate the total electromagnetic force acting on a structure made up of conductors and ferromagnetic materials. Two methods of calculation are given in this section. The first is the Maxwell stress method, which also provides a useful physical picture of the mechanism of force production. The second is an energy method, which complements the Maxwell stress method for purposes of calculations, but is less useful as a physical explanation.

The Maxwell stress concept

There is a sound scientific basis to the elementary idea that the magnetic lines of force are like rubber bands tending to draw pieces of iron together. The idea of lines or tubes of force was central to Faraday's conception of the magnetic field, but it was Maxwell who gave precise mathematical expression to this concept. Maxwell showed, as a deduction from the equations of the electromagnetic field, that magnetic forces could be considered to be transmitted through space (or a non-magnetic material) by the following system of stresses [3, 5]

(a) a tensile stress of magnitude $\frac{1}{2}BH$ newtons per square metre along the lines of force
(b) a compressive stress, also of magnitude $\frac{1}{2}BH$ newtons per square metre, at right angles to the lines of force.

Since $B = \mu_0 H$ in a non-magnetic medium, the stresses may also be written as $\frac{1}{2}\mu_0 H^2$ or $B^2/2\mu_0$.

If the magnetic field is perpendicular to the surface of a body (figure 1.12), there will be a tensile stress of magnitude $B^2/2\mu_0$, also perpendicular to the surface, drawing the surface into the field. If the field is parallel to the surface (figure 1.13), there will be a compressive stress of magnitude $B^2/2\mu_0$ pushing the surface out of the field. In the general case, when the flux density B makes an angle θ with the normal n, the stress t makes an angle 2θ with n (figure 1.14). The magnitude of t is still $B^2/2\mu_0$, and the three vectors n, B and t are coplanar.

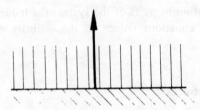

Figure 1.12   Magnetic force: field perpendicular to the surface

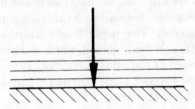

Figure 1.13   Magnetic force: field parallel to the surface

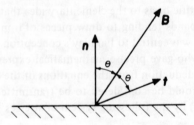

Figure 1.14   Maxwell stress vector

The force on an element of area δA is thus in the direction of t, and its magnitude is given by

$$\delta F = t\, \delta A = \frac{B^2}{2\mu_0}\, \delta A \text{ newtons} \tag{1.41}$$

An interesting, and at first sight surprising, deduction is that the force will be parallel to the surface when the field is inclined at 45°.

It is sometimes useful to relate the components of stress to the components of flux density, which may be done by resolving the vectors in directions normal and tangential to the surface. Thus if B_n and B_s are respectively the normal and tangential components of B, the normal component of stress is given by

$$t_n = \frac{1}{2\mu_0}(B_n^2 - B_s^2) \tag{1.42}$$

and the tangential component is

$$t_s = \frac{B_n B_s}{\mu_0} \tag{1.43}$$

Although the Maxwell stress concept has been introduced in terms of magnetised iron parts, it is not restricted to this situation. The electromagnetic force acting on any combination of iron parts and conductors may be found from the Maxwell stress on a surface enclosing the bodies; the only restriction is that the surface should not pass through any magnetised parts. The concept gives an immediate qualitative picture of the way in which forces are distributed over the surface of an object in a magnetic field; it will be applied to DC machines in chapter 2 and AC machines in chapter 4.

Calculation of the force from the Maxwell stress

Equations (1.42) and (1.43) may be integrated over the surface to give the total force on an object; this presupposes that an accurate field solution is available, for example by numerical analysis [6]. When such a solution is not available, it is still possible to calculate the force approximately from the Maxwell stress. Two examples will illustrate the method.

Force of attraction

Figure 1.15 shows an electromagnet lifting an iron bar, and the problem is to calculate the force of attraction. The actual field pattern is quite complex; it would be very tedious first to solve the field equations with the boundary conditions imposed by the structure, and then to integrate the stress over the surface to find the force. A good approximation can be obtained from the following considerations. If the airgaps between the magnet poles and the bar are small, and the permeability of the magnetic material is high, the magnetic

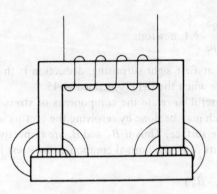

Figure 1.15   Electromagnet: actual field pattern

field in the gaps will be nearly uniform and much more intense than the fringing
field outside the airgaps. (This will be justified formally in section 1.6.) Since
the Maxwell stress varies as B^2, the field outside the airgaps will contribute very
little to the total force, and it may be ignored. For the purpose of calculating
the force, we may therefore replace the actual field distribution of figure 1.15
with the idealised distribution of figure 1.16, in which the field is uniform, confined to the airgaps and normal to the iron surfaces. If the area of each pole face
is A square metres, and the magnetic flux density in each airgap is B teslas, the
total force is

$$F = \frac{B^2}{2\mu_0} \cdot 2A = \frac{AB^2}{\mu_0} \text{ newtons} \qquad (1.44)$$

A method of calculating the flux density from the coil current and the dimensions of the magnet will be given in section 1.6.

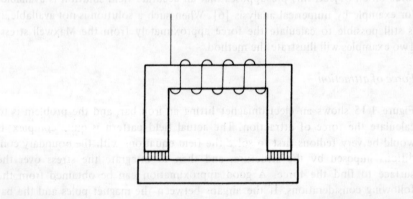

Figure 1.16   Electromagnet: idealised field pattern

Alignment torque

Consider the torque tending to rotate the short iron bar in figure 1.17 into alignment with the poles of the electromagnet. The permeability of the iron is assumed to be very high (ideally, infinite), so that the magnetic field is always normal to the iron surface. Evidently it is the stresses acting on the flat portions X and Y of the iron surface that are tending to rotate the bar; but the field here is particularly difficult to calculate.

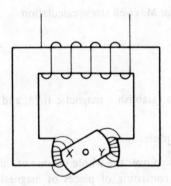

Figure 1.17 Alignment torque on an iron rotor

This is an example of a problem which requires another analytical device. The integral of the Maxwell stress over any surface surrounding a magnetic object gives the correct value for the total force on the object, even though the distribution of the force over this surface is quite different from the distribution over the surface of the object. To apply this to the alignment problem, observe that the field in the narrow airgap is practically uniform and can be calculated by the methods of section 1.6. Choose a surface such as JKGFLMHE (figure 1.18), and ignore the field between F and G and between E and H. The portions EJ, FL, KG and MH are perpendicular to the field; there will be tensile forces on these surfaces which cancel out in pairs. Since the field is negligible between F and G, and between E and H, there is no force on the portions FG and EH. The portions JK and LM are both parallel to the field; there will be compressive stresses on these surfaces tending to rotate the surface, and hence the bar, in a clockwise direction. If JK = LM = g and the depth of the bar is d, the force on each surface is

$$F = \frac{B^2}{2\mu_0} \cdot gd \text{ newtons}$$

and if a is the mean distance from the pivot to the airgap, the torque is

$$T = 2Fa = adgB^2/\mu_0 \text{ newton metres} \tag{1.45}$$

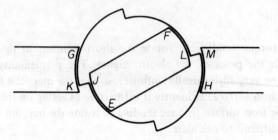

Figure 1.18   Surface for Maxwell stress calculation

Energy methods

Work must be done to establish a magnetic field, and the energy stored in the field is given by

$$W_m = \int \tfrac{1}{2} BH \, dv \text{ joules} \tag{1.46}$$

where the integral is taken over the whole volume of the field.

Consider a system consisting of pieces of magnetic material together with coils or conductors carrying currents. In general there will be electromagnetic forces acting on the various parts of the system, and if any part is displaced the force will do work. Let there be a small displacement δx in some part of the system. If the component of force in the direction of the displacement is F_x, the work done will be

$$\delta W = F_x \, \delta x \tag{1.47}$$

During this displacement there may be an increase δW_m in the stored magnetic energy, and if voltages are induced in any of the coils the electrical sources will have to supply an amount of energy δW_e. We thus have

$$\text{energy supplied} = \frac{\text{increase in}}{\text{stored energy}} + \text{work done}$$

so that

$$\delta W_e = \delta W_m + \delta W$$
$$= \delta W_m + F_x \, \delta x \tag{1.48}$$

If the currents in the coils are adjusted continuously during the displacement so that there is no change in the flux linkages, there will be no induced voltages; consequently the energy supplied, δW_e, will be zero. The work done by the force must come from the energy stored in the field

$$F_x \, \delta x = -\delta W_m$$

so that

$$F_x = -\frac{\partial W_\mathrm{m}}{\partial x}\bigg|_{\text{constant flux}} \tag{1.49}$$

When there is a linear relationship between flux and current another expression may be obtained. If the currents in all the coils are held constant during the displacement, it may be shown [3] that the energy δW_e supplied by the sources is equally divided between the mechanical work $F_x\,\delta x$ and the increase in stored energy δW_m. Thus

$$F_x\,\delta x = \delta W_\mathrm{m}$$

so that

$$F_x = +\frac{\partial W_\mathrm{m}}{\partial x}\bigg|_{\text{constant current}} \tag{1.50}$$

The force will be in newtons when the displacement is in metres and the field energy is in joules. Similar equations hold for rotational motion if F_x is replaced by the torque T_θ (in newton metres) and x is replaced by the angular displacement θ (in radians).

Calculation of the force on an iron part

As an example of the use of these expressions, consider once again the electromagnet shown in figure 1.16. If x is the displacement of the bar from the poles, the field energy is given by

$$\begin{aligned}
W_\mathrm{m} &= \int_{\text{airgap}} \tfrac{1}{2}BH\,\mathrm{d}v + \int_{\text{core}} \tfrac{1}{2}BH\,\mathrm{d}v\\
&= \frac{B^2 Ax}{\mu_0} + \int_{\text{core}} \tfrac{1}{2}BH\,\mathrm{d}v \quad \text{joules}
\end{aligned} \tag{1.51}$$

If the flux linkage is constant, B will be constant and the energy stored in the core will also be constant. Therefore

$$F_x = -\frac{\partial W_\mathrm{m}}{\partial x}\bigg|_{\text{constant flux}} = -\frac{B^2 A}{\mu_0} \quad \text{newtons} \tag{1.52}$$

This is numerically the same as eqn (1.44) obtained from the Maxwell stress, and the negative sign shows that the force on the bar is in the direction of decreasing x, that is, upwards. Here the Maxwell stress method is obviously simpler, and Carpenter [7] has shown this to be true generally for calculating forces on iron surfaces.

Energy and inductance

With a single coil carrying a current i, the energy stored in the magnetic field is given by

$$W_m = \tfrac{1}{2}Li^2 \qquad (1.53)$$

If the motion of a part of the system causes a change in the inductance, then eqn (1.50) gives

$$F_x = \left. \frac{\partial W_m}{\partial x} \right|_{\text{constant current}} = \tfrac{1}{2}i^2 \frac{\partial L}{\partial x} \qquad (1.54)$$

This is an important and useful result, for it shows that the mechanical force can be expressed in terms of the variation in the inductance coefficient L, a quantity which can be measured electrically.

With a pair of mutually coupled coils carrying currents i_1 and i_2, the stored magnetic energy is given by

$$W_m = \tfrac{1}{2}L_1 i_1^2 + \tfrac{1}{2}L_2 i_2^2 + M i_1 i_2 \qquad (1.55)$$

The force acting on a part of the system is then given by

$$F_x = \tfrac{1}{2}i_1^2 \frac{\partial L_1}{\partial x} + \tfrac{1}{2}i_2^2 \frac{\partial L_2}{\partial x} + i_1 i_2 \frac{\partial M}{\partial x} \qquad (1.56)$$

Similar expressions hold for torque in terms of angular displacement.

Calculation of the torque on an air-cored coil

As an example of the application of eqn (1.56), consider the coil system of an electrodynamic wattmeter, shown in figure 1.19. A small moving coil is mounted on pivots midway between two fixed coils. The fixed coils are connected in series, and are separated by a distance equal to their radius; this is a Helmholtz pair, which produces in the vicinity of the moving coil a nearly uniform magnetic field parallel to the common axis of the fixed coils. If each fixed coil has N_1 turns and carries a current i_1 amperes, the flux density is

$$B = \frac{8\mu_0 N_1 i_1}{5\sqrt{5}r} \text{ teslas} \qquad (1.57)$$

where r is the radius in metres.

If the moving coil has N_2 turns and an area A square metres, the flux linking it is

$$\psi_{21} = N_2 AB \cos\theta \text{ webers} \qquad (1.58)$$

and the mutual inductance between the fixed and moving coils is

$$M = \frac{\psi_{21}}{i_1} = \frac{8\mu_0}{5\sqrt{5}} \cdot \frac{N_1 N_2 A}{r} \cos\theta \text{ henrys} \qquad (1.59)$$

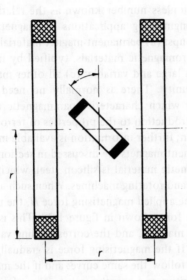

Figure 1.19 Coil system for an electrodynamic wattmeter

Since the self-inductances are independent of θ, the torque on the moving coil is

$$T = i_1 i_2 \frac{\partial M}{\partial \theta} = -\frac{8\mu_0}{5\sqrt{5}} \cdot \frac{N_1 N_2 A}{r} i_1 i_2 \sin\theta \text{ newton metres} \qquad (1.60)$$

This is an instance of an energy method giving a straightforward calculation of the torque, whereas the Maxwell stress would be difficult to evaluate.

1.5 Magnetic materials

In free space the magnetic flux density B is related to the magnetising force H by the expression

$$B = \mu_0 H \qquad (1.61)$$

where μ_0 is the primary magnetic constant (with a value of $4\pi \times 10^{-7}$ H/m).

This relationship is modified in a material medium; if we exclude permanent-magnet materials, eqn (1.61) becomes

$$B = \mu_0 \mu_r H \tag{1.62}$$

where μ_r is a dimensionless number known as the relative permeability of the material. For most engineering applications of magnetism, materials may be divided into three groups: (a) permanent-magnet materials, for which eqn (1.62) does not hold; (b) ferromagnetic materials, typified by iron, for which the relative permeability μ_r is large and variable; (c) all other materials, for which μ_r is practically equal to unity. There is normally no need to consider the small deviations from unity which characterise paramagnetic and diamagnetic behaviour. Only a brief introduction to the properties of ferromagnetic materials will be given in this section; further information is available in standard texts such as Brailsford [8]. Permanent magnets are discussed in section 1.7.

A typical ferromagnetic material is silicon steel, which is widely used for the cores of transformers and rotating machines. When such a material is magnetised by slowly increasing the applied magnetising force H, the resulting flux density B follows a curve of the form shown in figure 1.20. This is known as the *magnetisation curve* for the material, and the corresponding variation of μ_r with B is shown in figure 1.21. If the magnetising force is gradually reduced to zero, the flux density does not follow the same curve; and if the magnetising force slowly alternates between positive and negative values, the relationship between B and H takes the form of a hysteresis loop as shown in figure 1.22. When the amplitude of the alternating magnetising force is changed, a new hysteresis loop will be formed; the locus of the tips of these loops is the magnetisation curve shown in figure 1.20.

The part of the magnetisation curve where the slope begins to change rapidly is termed the *knee*. Below the knee it is often possible to use a linear approximation to the actual characteristic, with a corresponding constant value for the relative permeability. But the onset of saturation above the knee marks a dramatic change in the properties of the material, which must be recognised in the design and analysis of magnetic structures.

Hysteresis loss

When a magnetic material is taken through a cycle of magnetisation, energy is dissipated in the material in the form of heat. This is known as the *hysteresis loss*, and it may be shown [3] that the energy loss per unit volume for each cycle of magnetisation is equal to the area of the hysteresis loop. The area of the loop will depend on the nature of the material and the value of B_{max} (figure 1.22), and an approximate empirical relationship discovered by Steinmetz is

$$w_h = \lambda_h B_{max}^n \text{ joules/metre}^3 \tag{1.63}$$

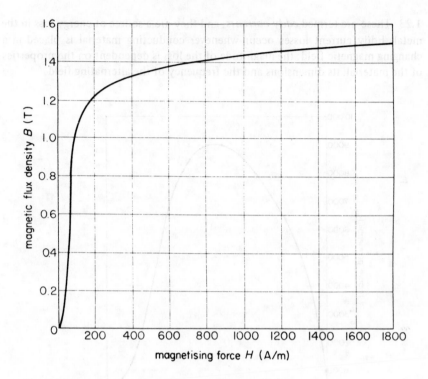

Figure 1.20   Magnetisation curve for 4 per cent silicon steel

In this expression w_h is the loss per unit volume for each cycle of magnetisation; the index n has a value of about 1.7 for many materials; and the coefficient λ_h is a property of the material, with typical values of 500 for 4 per cent silicon steel and 3000 for cast iron.

When the material is subjected to an alternating magnetic field of constant amplitude there will be a constant energy loss per cycle, and the power absorbed is therefore proportional to the frequency. Assuming the Steinmetz law, we have the following expression for the hysteresis loss per unit volume

$$p_h = \lambda_h B_{max}^{1.7} f \text{ watts/metre}^3 \tag{1.64}$$

where f is the frequency in hertz.

Eddy current loss

If a closed loop of wire is placed in an alternating magnetic field, the induced EMF will circulate a current round the loop. A solid block of metal will likewise have circulating currents induced in it by an alternating field, as shown in figure

1.23. These are termed *eddy currents*, and they are a source of energy loss in the metal. Eddy current losses occur whenever conducting material is placed in a changing magnetic field; the magnitude of the loss is dependent on the properties of the material, its dimensions and the frequency of the alternating field.

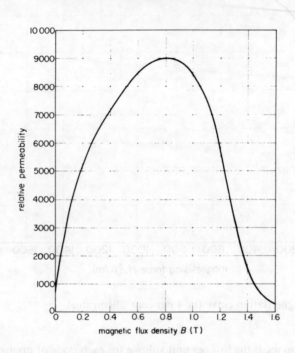

Figure 1.21   Relative permeability of 4 per cent silicon steel

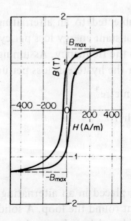

Figure 1.22   Hysteresis loop for 4 per cent silicon steel

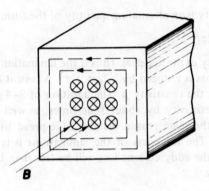

Figure 1.23 Eddy currents in a solid conductor

Magnetic structures carrying alternating magnetic flux are usually made from a stack of thin plates or laminations, separated from one another by a layer of insulation (figure 12.4). This construction breaks up the eddy current paths, with a consequent reduction in the loss; qualitatively, the effect may be explained as follows. With solid metal (figure 1.23) the currents would flow in approximately square paths; these paths enclose a large area for a given perimeter, and the induced EMF is high for a path of given resistance. When the metal is divided into laminations (figure 1.24), the current paths are long narrow rectangles; the area enclosed by a given perimeter is much smaller, and the induced EMF is smaller, giving lower currents and reduced losses. An approximate analysis [3, 8] shows that in plates of thickness t (where t is much smaller than the width or length) the eddy current loss per unit volume is given by

$$p_e = \frac{\pi^2 B_{max}^2 f^2 t^2}{6\rho} \quad \text{watts/metre}^3 \tag{1.65}$$

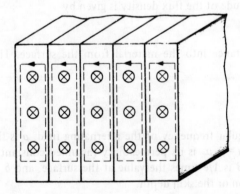

Figure 1.24 Eddy currents in a laminated conductor

where the flux density is an alternating quantity of the form

$$B = B_{max} \sin 2\pi ft \qquad (1.66)$$

and ρ is the resistivity of the material. Thus if the lamination thickness is reduced by a factor x, the loss is reduced by a factor x^2. As might be expected, the loss varies inversely with the resistivity ρ. The addition of 3–4 per cent of silicon to iron increases the resistivity by about four times, as well as reducing the hysteresis loss; this is the main reason for the widespread use of silicon steel in electrical machines. The thickness of the laminations is typically 0.3–0.5 mm, which ensures that the eddy current loss will be less than the hysteresis loss at a frequency of 50 Hz.

Skin effect

The eddy currents in a bar such as the one shown in figure 1.23 will produce a magnetic field within the bar which, by Lenz's law, will oppose the applied field. Thus the magnetic flux density will fall from a value B_0 at the surface to some lower value in the interior. The effect depends on the properties of the material, the frequency of the alternating field and the dimensions of the bar. It is possible for the magnitude of the flux density to fall very rapidly in the interior of the bar, so that most of the flux is confined to a thin layer or skin near the surface. The phenomenon is termed *skin effect*, and it implies very inefficient use of the magnetic material (quite apart from any eddy current losses). A similar effect occurs in conductors carrying alternating current, where the current density falls from some value J_0 at the surface to a lower value in the interior.

The variation of flux density with distance may be calculated by solving the electromagnetic field equations [9]. When skin effect is well developed, so that the flux density decays rapidly, the solution is independent of the geometry of the bar; the magnitude of the flux density is given by

$$B = B_0 e^{-x/\delta} \qquad (1.67)$$

where x is the distance into the material from the surface. The quantity δ is given by

$$\delta = \sqrt{\frac{2\rho}{\mu\omega}} \qquad (1.68)$$

where ω is the angular frequency of the alternating field, ρ is the resistivity of the material and $\mu = \mu_0\mu_r$ is its permeability (assumed constant). At a depth δ the magnitude of B is $1/e$ times the value at the surface, and δ is known as the depth of penetration or the skin depth.

The phenomenon of skin effect gives a second reason for using laminated magnetic circuits. If the thickness of a plate is much more than twice the depth of penetration δ, the central region will carry very little flux. The material will be fully utilised if it is divided into laminations less than δ in thickness, for the flux density will then be fairly uniform across the lamination. The depth of penetration in silicon steel is about 1 mm at a frequency of 50 Hz, so the typical lamination thickness of 0.5 mm ensures that skin effect will not be significant.

1.6 The magnetic circuit

In the study of electromagnetic devices, it is often necessary to determine the magnetic field from a knowledge of the structure of the device and the magnitudes of the currents flowing in coils or other conductors. An accurate determination involves the solution of the partial differential equations of the electromagnetic field, a problem which is made more difficult by the non-linear properties of magnetic materials. Modern computational methods [6] can determine the field to any desired degree of accuracy, but a simple method of estimating the field is also required. The magnetic circuit concept provides an approximate method of solution which is good enough for many purposes and gives some immediate physical insight into the behaviour of magnetic structures.

The magnetic circuit concept

Figure 1.25 shows a closed iron core magnetised by a coil carrying a current. If the relative permeability of the iron is high, most of the magnetic flux will be

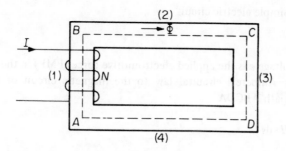

Figure 1.25 Simple magnetic circuit

confined to the iron. The flux Φ through any cross-section of the core will then be substantially the same; this follows from the fact that the flux of B out of any closed surface is zero; if there is no flux out of the sides of the iron, the flux entering a section must be equal to the flux leaving it. We thus have an analogy with a simple electric circuit (figure 1.26), in which the current i (which is the flux of the current density $\boldsymbol{J}$) is the same for all cross-sections of the conductor. Corresponding to Kirchhoff's current law $\Sigma i = 0$ we have the flux law $\Sigma \Phi = 0$, and the structure of figure 1.25 is known as a *magnetic circuit*. We shall see that there is a very close analogy between the analysis of the electric and magnetic circuits.

Apply Kirchhoff's voltage law to the electric circuit of figure 1.26, following the path PQRST

$$e = -\Sigma v$$

$$= -(v_{PQ} + v_{QR} + v_{RS} + v_{ST}) \tag{1.69}$$

$$= \int_P^Q \boldsymbol{E} \cdot d\boldsymbol{s} + \int_Q^R \boldsymbol{E} \cdot d\boldsymbol{s} + \int_R^S \boldsymbol{E} \cdot d\boldsymbol{s} + \int_S^T \boldsymbol{E} \cdot d\boldsymbol{s} \tag{1.70}$$

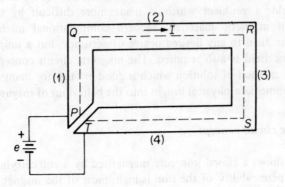

Figure 1.26 Simple electric circuit

The battery voltage e is the applied electromotive force (EMF) in the circuit.

Now apply Ampère's circuital law to the magnetic circuit of figure 1.25, following the path ABCDA

$$NI = \oint \boldsymbol{H} \cdot d\boldsymbol{s}$$

$$= \int_A^B \boldsymbol{H} \cdot d\boldsymbol{s} + \int_B^C \boldsymbol{H} \cdot d\boldsymbol{s} + \int_C^D \boldsymbol{H} \cdot d\boldsymbol{s} + \int_D^A \boldsymbol{H} \cdot d\boldsymbol{s} \tag{1.71}$$

Note the similarity between eqns (1.70) and (1.71). Just as the quantity

$$v_{PQ} = -\int_P^Q \boldsymbol{E} \cdot d\boldsymbol{s}$$

is the electric potential difference between P and Q, the quantity

$$U_{AB} = - \int_A^B H \cdot ds$$

is the magnetic potential difference between A and B. If we now put $NI = F$ (note that the symbol F in this context does not represent mechanical force), eqn (1.71) becomes

$$F = \oint H \cdot ds$$

$$= - (U_{AB} + U_{BC} + U_{CD} + U_{DA})$$

$$= - \Sigma U \tag{1.72}$$

and eqn (1.72) is the magnetic counterpart of Kirchhoff's voltage law (eqn 1.69). By analogy with the electromotive force, the quantity $F = NI$ is known as the magnetomotive force (MMF), measured in amperes (A). It follows that the units of magnetic potential, U, are also amperes.

Electric and magnetic circuit analogies

The analogy can be taken a stage further. In figure 1.26, suppose that limb (1) has a length l_1, a cross-sectional area A_1, and a constant conductivity σ_1. Since the electric field is practically uniform

$$\int_P^Q E \cdot ds = E_1 l_1$$

$$= \frac{J_1 l_1}{\sigma_1}$$

$$= \frac{i l_1}{\sigma_1 A_1}$$

$$= i R_1$$

where R_1 is the resistance of limb (1) given by

$$R_1 = \frac{l_1}{\sigma_1 A_1} \text{ ohms} \tag{1.73}$$

Thus eqn (1.70) becomes

$$e = i(R_1 + R_2 + R_3 + R_4) \tag{1.74}$$

In figure 1.25, suppose likewise that limb (1) has a length l_1, a cross-sectional area A_1, and a constant permeability μ_1 (where $\mu = \mu_0 \mu_r$). Since the magnetic field is practically uniform

$$\int_A^B H \cdot ds = H_1 l_1$$

$$= \frac{B_1 l_1}{\mu_1}$$

$$= \frac{\Phi l_1}{\mu_1 A_1}$$

$$= \Phi S_1$$

where S_1 is known as the *reluctance* of limb (1) and is given by

$$S_1 = \frac{l_1}{\mu_1 A_1} \quad \text{amperes/weber} \tag{1.75}$$

Thus eqn (1.71) becomes

$$NI = F = \Phi(S_1 + S_2 + S_3 + S_4) \tag{1.76}$$

The similarity between eqns (1.73) and (1.75), and between eqns (1.74) and (1.76) should be noted. It follows that the electric and magnetic circuits may be represented by the circuit diagrams of figures 1.27 and 1.28. Table 1.1 summarises the analogy between electric and magnetic circuits.

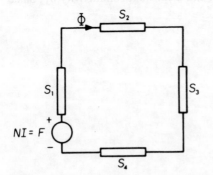
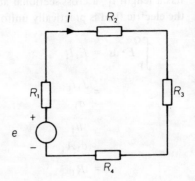

Figure 1.27 Magnetic circuit diagram   Figure 1.28   Electric circuit diagram

Simple magnetic circuits with airgaps

An example will illustrate the methods of analysing a simple magnetic circuit. Figure 1.29 shows an electromagnet consisting of an iron core with an airgap. The coil carries a current of 1 A, and we wish to find the number of turns required to set up a flux density of 1.2 T in the airgap. A simple method is to

Table 1.1. Electric and magnetic circuit analogies

Electric circuit	Magnetic circuit
Electromotive force e	Magnetomotive force F
Electric current i	Magnetic flux Φ
Electric potential difference v	Magnetic potential difference U
Resistance $R = v/i = l/\sigma A$	Reluctance $S = U/\Phi = l/\mu A$
Current law $\Sigma i = 0$	Flux law $\Sigma \Phi = 0$
Voltage law $\Sigma(e + v) = 0$	Circuital law $\Sigma(F + U) = 0$

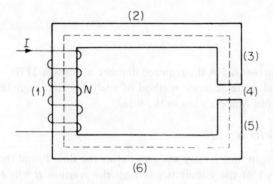

Figure 1.29 Electromagnet with an airgap

assume a constant value for the permeability of the core, and then to calculate the reluctances of the various parts of the magnetic circuit. If the core material is silicon steel, figure 1.21 shows that the relative permeability exceeds 3000 for a wide range of flux densities below the knee of the magnetisation curve. Table 1.2 gives the dimensions of the magnetic circuit and the calculated results with a value of 3000 for the relative permeability of the core. The flux in the core is given by

$$\Phi = BA = 1.2 \times 100 \times 10^{-6} \text{ Wb}$$
$$= 120 \ \mu\text{Wb}$$

and the MMF is therefore

$$F = \Phi S = 120 \times 10^{-6} \times 17.9 \times 10^{6} \text{ A}$$
$$= 2170 \text{ A}$$

Table 1.2. Magnetic circuit calculation using constant permeability

Section of circuit	(1)	(2)	(3)	(4)	(5)	(6)
Material	iron	iron	iron	air	iron	iron
Relative permeability μ_r	3000	3000	3000	1	3000	3000
length l (mm)	150	250	74	2	74	250
Area A (mm^2)	80	125	100	100	100	125
Reluctance $S = l/\mu_0\mu_r A$ (MA/Wb)	0.05	0.53	0.20	15.9	0.20	0.53

$$
\begin{aligned}
\text{Reluctance of iron path} &= 1.96 \text{ MA/Wb} \\
\text{Reluctance of airgap} &= 15.9 \text{ MA/Wb} \\
\text{Total reluctance} &= 17.9 \text{ MA/Wb}
\end{aligned}
$$

Since the coil current is 1 A the required number of turns is 2170.

A second and more accurate method of analysing the magnetic circuit is to work directly from Ampère's law in the form

$$F = NI = \oint H \cdot ds = \Sigma Hl \tag{1.77}$$

The specified airgap flux density and area define the flux Φ, and the flux density in any other part of the circuit is given by the relation $B = \Phi/A$. The corresponding value of H may be found from the magnetisation curve for the material used in that part of the circuit, and the sum of the Hl terms may then be computed. Table 1.3 shows the calculation; the value of H in the airgap is obtained from the relation $B = \mu_0 H$; the magnetisation curve of figure 1.20 is used for the iron parts; and the flux is given by $\Phi = BA = 120\ \mu$Wb. The number of turns required on the coil is therefore 2250, and the total reluctance given by this calculation is

$$S = F/\Phi = 18.7 \text{ MA/Wb}$$

This reluctance is larger than the previous result of 17.9 MA/Wb. Table 1.3 shows that section (1) of the magnetic circuit has been driven into saturation, with a flux density of 1.5 T; this results in an excessive potential drop in the section, with a corresponding increase in the total reluctance. If the airgap flux density is reduced to 1.0 T, section (1) will come out of saturation with a flux density of 1.25 T. The whole iron path is then unsaturated, and a similar calculation gives a value of 16.7 MA/Wb for the total reluctance. This is smaller than the value of 17.9 MA/Wb calculated on the assumption of a constant permeability of 3000, because the relative permeability of most parts of the circuit is now greater than 3000, but the error is not large.

Table 1.3. Magnetic circuit calculation using the magnetisation curve

Section of circuit	(1)	(2)	(3)	(4)	(5)	(6)
Material	iron	iron	iron	air	iron	iron
Area A (mm^2)	80	125	100	100	100	125
Flux density $B = \Phi/A$ (T)	1.5	0.96	1.2	1.2	1.2	0.96
Magnetising force H (A/m)	1800	90	170	954×10^3	170	90
Length l (mm)	150	250	74	2	74	250
Potential drop Hl (A)	270	22.5	12.6	1910	12.6	22.5

Potential drop in iron   =   340 A
Potential drop in airgap = 1910 A
Total potential drop = F = 2250 A

Linearity

In the example just considered the iron path is nearly 400 times the length of the airgap, but it contributes only about 10 per cent of the total reluctance of the magnetic circuit. Thus when the iron is unsaturated quite a small airgap will have a dominant effect, and any changes in the magnetic condition of the core will cause very little change in the total reluctance. Since $NI = \Phi S$, it follows that the flux will be proportional to the current if the total reluctance is constant, and this is the basis of the assumption of linearity made earlier in the chapter. There are two situations in which the relationship between flux and current is not even approximately linear. If there are no airgaps in the magnetic circuit, there will be no constant reluctance term to swamp the variable reluctance of the iron, and the relationship between flux and current will be determined by the magnetisation curve of the material. If there are airgaps but the iron is driven into saturation, the relative permeability of the iron will be low (see figure 1.21) and its reluctance may be comparable to the reluctance of the airgaps; the non-linear iron characteristic will again make its presence felt. The reader is invited to explore these effects in problem 1.8 at the end of the chapter.

Fringing and leakage

In the analysis of a magnetic circuit with an airgap, two assumptions have been made in order to simplify the calculation

(1) flux passes straight across the airgap, without spreading into the surrounding air
(2) there is no leakage of flux from the iron path into the surrounding air.

In practice, there is some spreading of the airgap flux (known as *fringing*), and leakage cannot be neglected when the airgap is large (that is, when its length is not negligible in comparison with the other air spaces between the iron parts). Both of these effects are illustrated in figure 1.30. It is possible to introduce fringing and leakage coefficients to take account of these effects, thereby extending the magnetic circuit theory to handle quite complex problems without having to resort to a full field analysis [10].

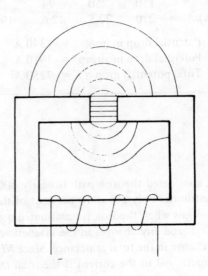

Figure 1.30   Fringing and leakage flux

Magnetic circuits with parallel paths

Figure 1.31 shows a magnetic circuit with parallel paths. A simple analysis is possible if we assume that the permeability is constant, and also neglect leakage and fringing. The circuit can then be represented by the diagram of figure 1.32, where S_a and S_i are the constant reluctances of the air and iron paths. Applying the flux law to the junction P gives $\Phi_3 = \Phi_1 + \Phi_2$, and applying the circuital law in the form $F = -\Sigma U = \Sigma \Phi S$ to meshes (1) and (2) gives

$$F = S_{i_3}(\Phi_1 + \Phi_2) + (S_{a_1} + S_{i_1})\Phi_1 \tag{1.78}$$

$$F = S_{i_3}(\Phi_1 + \Phi_2) + (S_{a_2} + S_{i_2})\Phi_2 \tag{1.79}$$

Equations (1.78) and (1.79) can be solved to find Φ_1 and Φ_2. Note that this is exactly analogous to applying Kirchhoff's voltage law in the form $e = \Sigma iR$ to the two meshes of a similar electric circuit. More complex magnetic circuits may be handled in a similar way, making full use of any relevant electric circuit theorems.

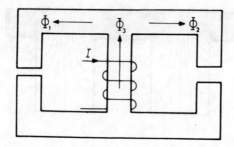

Figure 1.31 Magnetic circuit with parallel paths

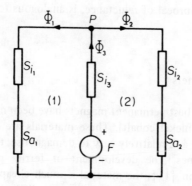

Figure 1.32 Magnetic circuit diagram for figure 1.31

Magnetic circuits: concluding remarks

The circuit analogy is a useful device for deducing the properties of magnetic structures from the more familiar properties of electric circuits. An EMF drives a current through an electric circuit against the resistance; an MMF drives a flux through a magnetic circuit against the reluctance, and the greater the reluctance the greater the MMF required to establish the flux. Just as current takes the path of least resistance, flux takes the path of least reluctance. In magnetic circuits with small airgaps the flux will be concentrated in the low-reluctance region of the gap, and the fringing field beyond the gap will fall away rapidly as the length of the air path increases. Figure 1.33 shows a type of structure commonly found in electrical machines, and it is immediately evident that the flux will be concentrated in the teeth, leaving a relatively weak field in the slots. An approximate calculation follows from the electric circuit rule for current division in parallel

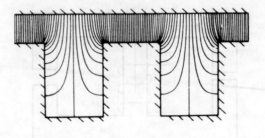

Figure 1.33　Field in electrical machine slots

branches: the flux will divide in the ratio of the permeances, where permeance (symbol Λ), the reciprocal of reluctance, is analogous to the conductance of an electric circuit.

1.7 Permanent magnets

For many years the best permanent magnets have been made from alloys such as Alnico (aluminium–nickel–cobalt). These materials are expensive, brittle, difficult to manufacture and relatively easy to demagnetise; they are not widely used in electrical machines. The development of ferrite permanent magnets has changed this position [11]; the material is much cheaper, it is easier to manufacture in special shapes, and it is much more difficult to demagnetise. More recently, new permanent-magnet materials based on alloys of cobalt and rare-earth elements have been developed; the best known of these is samarium–cobalt (SmCo), which has much better magnetic properties than ferrites, but is very expensive [11]. In spite of the cost, SmCo has been used in small electrical machines in increasing quantities, to the extent that supplies of the raw materials are becoming scarce. The latest development is neodymium–iron–boron (NdFeB) [11], which has better magnetic properties than SmCo, is considerably cheaper and has more abundant sources of raw materials. This material is already having a profound effect on the design of small electrical machines, and its use is likely to increase. The principal disadvantage of NdFeB is the variation of its properties with temperature; it has much larger temperature coefficients than SmCo, and it exhibits an irreversible loss of magnetisation at high temperatures. Early samples were limited to temperatures below 125°C, but new alloys extend this limit to about 200°C.

The magnetic circuit concept applies equally well when the source of the magnetic field is a permanent magnet instead of a current-carrying coil. Figure 1.34 shows such a circuit, where iron pole-pieces guide the flux from the magnet to the airgap. The permanent magnet has a length l_m and a cross-sectional area A_m; the airgap has a length l_g and a cross-sectional area A_g. To simplify the analysis, assume that the pole-pieces have negligible reluctance, and that there is

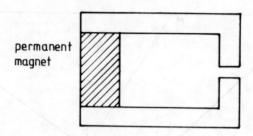

Figure 1.34 Permanent magnet with an airgap

negligible leakage or fringing. Since the flux is constant round the circuit, we have

$$B_m A_m = B_g A_g \tag{1.80}$$

There is no current, so Ampère's circuital law gives

$$0 = \oint H \cdot ds = H_m l_m + H_g l_g$$
$$= H_m l_m + B_g l_g / \mu_0 \tag{1.81}$$

Combining eqns (1.80) and (1.81) gives

$$B_m = -\mu_0 \frac{l_m A_g}{l_g A_m} H_m \tag{1.82}$$

This is a straight-line relationship between B_m and H_m imposed by the magnetic circuit. But the material of the permanent magnet also has its own inherent relationship between B_m and H_m, shown in the hysteresis loop for the material, and the portion of interest is the second quadrant where B is positive and H is negative. This part of the loop is termed the *demagnetisation characteristic*.

Figure 1.35 shows the demagnetisation characteristic for one type of NdFeB permanent-magnet material [12]. The quantity B_r is known as the *remanence*; it is the flux density which remains in the material when the positive magnetising force H is reduced to zero. The quantity H_c is termed the *coercivity*; it is the negative magnetising force which must be applied to reduce the flux density to zero. Also shown in figure 1.35 is a straight line OM plotted from eqn (1.82) for a particular magnetic circuit. This *load line* cuts the demagnetisation characteristic at P, which is the working point for the material in this magnetic circuit.

Suppose that the working point in figure 1.35 is moved from P to a lower point Q on the curve. This may be achieved by applying a reverse MMF with a current-carrying coil; or by increasing the length of the airgap in the magnetic circuit, to give a new load line ON. If a large reverse MMF is applied, the working point may be driven down to a point such as Q'. On removal of the demagnetis-

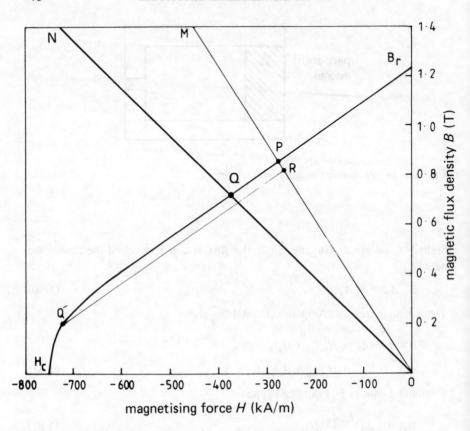

Figure 1.35 Demagnetisation characteristic for NeIGT 35 neodymium-iron-boron

ing influence – the reverse MMF or the large airgap – the working point may not return along the original curve to P. Instead the working point traverses a line Q'R, known as a *recoil line*, to a new working point R on the original load line OM. If a large demagnetising influence is applied, as can happen when an electrical machine is short-circuited, it is possible for the new working point R to be well below the original point P; this represents a partial demagnetisation of the material. Materials such as NdFeB, SmCo and some ferrites have a demagnetisation characteristic which is nearly a straight line. For these materials, the recoil line is almost indistinguishable from the original characteristic, and R is very close to P. With Alnico-type magnets and some ferrites, the characteristic is very non-linear; recoil is much more pronounced, and severe demagnetisation can easily occur.

Modern high-performance permanent-magnet materials are expensive, and it is desirable to minimise the volume of the magnet given by

$$V_m = A_m l_m \tag{1.83}$$

Substituting for A_m and l_m from eqns (1.80) and (1.81) gives

$$V_m = - \frac{B_g^2 A_g l_g}{\mu_0 B_m H_m} \tag{1.84}$$

Thus for a given airgap flux density B_g and volume $A_g l_g$, the volume of the magnetic material will be a minimum when the energy product $B_m H_m$ is a maximum. The value of B_m which gives the maximum energy product can be found from a graph of $B_m H_m$ against B_m; this defines the optimum working point, and the magnet dimensions can be calculated from eqns (1.80) and (1.81). Usually the desired airgap flux density B_g is greater than the optimum magnet flux density B_m; consequently the area A_g must be less than A_m, and the pole-pieces act as flux concentrators.

Problems

1.1. A flat copper plate is held in a vertical plane and then allowed to fall through the gap between the poles of a magnet. The plate is much wider than the poles, and any induced currents which flow in the part of the plate between the poles are assumed to find return paths of negligible resistance in the rest of the plate. The magnet poles are square, and the magnetic field may be assumed to be uniform and confined to the area of the poles. Show that the plate will experience a retarding force proportional to its velocity, and calculate the magnitude of the force when the velocity is 10 m/s. The thickness of the plate is 5 mm; the resistivity of copper is 1.68×10^{-8} Ω m; the magnet poles are 100 mm square; and the magnetic flux density is 1.0 T.

1.2. In the Faraday disc machine (section 1.2) there will be a torque on the disc when current flows between the centre and the periphery. By considering the torque on an elementary annular ring of the disc, show that the total torque is given by the expression

$$T = \tfrac{1}{2} Bia^2 \text{ newton metres}$$

where B is the magnetic flux density in teslas, i is the current in amperes and a is the radius of the disc in metres. Hence show that the mechanical power output from the disc is equal to the electrical power input when the machine runs as a motor. The resistance of the disc may be ignored.

1.3. Figure 1.36 shows an extract from a patent specification [13] for an improved type of DC generator. The rotor R is magnetised by the field coil F, and thus forms a rotating magnet. The inventors claim that the rotating field of this magnet will induce an EMF in a stationary conductor such as C, which forms one side of a rectangular coil. Several coils may be connected in series to increase the output voltage of the machine.

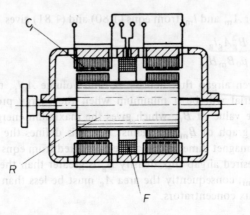

Figure 1.36 Proposed DC generator (reproduced with the permission of the Controller of Her Majesty's Stationery Office)

Some engineers have expressed doubts as to whether the machine will actually work. Settle the question by the application of Faraday's law.

1.4. Show that there can be no magnetic field outside a coaxial cable carrying a current. Hence show that an alternating magnetic field due to currents in other conductors will induce no voltage in the cable circuit.

1.5. A steel ring is uniformly wound with a coil of 1000 turns, and a flux density of 1.5 T is produced in the ring by a coil current of 3 A. If the ring has a mean diameter of 0.2 m and a cross-sectional area of 0.001 m^2, calculate the inductance of the coil.

The ring is divided into two equal parts by making cuts in the iron. The width of each cut is 2 mm, and the current in the coil is increased to maintain the original flux density of 1.5 T. Calculate (a) the new value of the coil current; (b) the new coil inductance; (c) the force of attraction between the two halves of the ring.

1.6. The device shown in figure 1.17 will function as an elementary form of AC motor when the coil carries a current of the form $i = I_m \cos \omega t$. The inductance of the coil depends on the rotor position and may be assumed to follow the law $L = L_1 + L_2 \cos 2\theta$, where θ is the angular position of the rotor. If the rotor revolves with a steady angular velocity ω_r, so that $\theta = \omega_r t + \phi$, show that the torque on the rotor is given by the expression

$$T = -\tfrac{1}{2} L_2 I_m^2 (1 + \cos 2\omega t) \sin (2\omega_r t + 2\phi)$$

Show that the torque will have an average value of zero unless $\omega_r = \omega$, and obtain an expression for the average value when this condition holds.

1.7. The following figures were obtained for the power loss in the core of a transformer at different frequencies, with the maximum value of the flux density held constant

frequency (Hz) 35 40 45 50 55 60 65 70
power loss (W) 46 54 62 70 78 87 96 105

If the loss is made up of hysteresis and eddy current components, show that the total loss should be related to the frequency by an expression of the form

$$P = Af + Bf^2$$

where A and B are constants. By plotting a graph of P/f against frequency, determine the constants A and B for the transformer, and hence find the values of the hysteresis and eddy current components of the core loss at a frequency of 50 Hz.

1.8. Assume that the ring in problem 1.5 is made from silicon steel, with the magnetisation curve shown in figure 1.20. Calculate the values of coil current required to give a number of values of flux density ranging from 0 to 1.5 T, (a) for a solid ring, (b) for a ring with a single airgap of 1 mm. Hence plot graphs of flux against current and inductance against current for the two cases.

1.9. For the magnetic circuit of figure 1.34, suppose that the demagnetisation characteristic of the permanent magnet is a straight line. Show that the magnet may be represented by an MMF $F_m = H_c l_m$ in series with a reluctance $S_m = l_m/\mu_m A_m$, where l_m is the length of the magnet, A_m is its cross-sectional area and $\mu_m = B_r/H_c$ is the slope of the demagnetisation characteristic.

References

1 P. Dunsheath, *A History of Electrical Engineering* (London: Faber, 1962).

2 J. R. Bumby, *Superconducting Rotating Electrical Machines* (Oxford University Press, 1983).

3 G. W. Carter, *The Electromagnetic Field in its Engineering Aspects*, 2nd ed. (London: Longman, 1967).

4 K. J. Binns, 'Flux cutting or flux linking', *J. IEE*, **9** (1970), p. 259.

5 J. A. Stratton, *Electromagnetic Theory* (New York: McGraw-Hill, 1941).

6 P. P. Silvester and R. L. Ferrari, *Finite Elements for Electrical Engineers*, 2nd ed. (Cambridge University Press, 1989).

7 C. J. Carpenter, 'Surface integral methods of calculating forces on magnetized iron parts', *Proc. IEE*, **107C** (1960), pp. 19–28.

8 F. Brailsford, *Physical Principles of Magnetism* (London: Van Nostrand, 1966).

9 R. L. Stoll, *The Analysis of Eddy Currents* (Oxford University Press, 1974).

10 Department of Electrical Engineering, Massachusetts Institute of Technology, *Magnetic Circuits and Transformers* (Cambridge, Mass: MIT Press, 1943).

11 M. McCaig and A. G. Clegg, *Permanent Magnets in Theory and Practice*, 2nd ed. (Plymouth: Pentech Press, 1987).
12 I G Technologies, Inc., *NeIGT Permanent Magnet Material* (I G Technologies, Inc., 1984).
13 W. Reiners and G. Wiggermann, *Improvements in or relating to Homopolar Induction Machinery*, British Patent 917 263 (1963).

2   Direct Current Machines

2.1 Introduction

Historically, DC machines were the first to be developed because the only available electrical power source was the DC voltaic cell. The advantages of alternating current were later recognised, and the invention of the induction motor was an important factor in securing acceptance of the alternating current system. The two main types of AC machine (synchronous and induction machines) are structurally simpler than DC machines; but the theory of AC machines is inherently more complex than the theory of DC machines, and we therefore adopt the historical order in developing the principles.

The homopolar machine mentioned in section 1.2 is a DC machine; in fact it is a pure DC machine, for we shall see that the conventional machine generates an alternating voltage which is rectified mechanically by the commutator. Before the advent of cryogenics, the homopolar machine was suitable only for certain low-voltage heavy-current applications, and the development of DC machines followed a different path. If a coil rotates in a magnetic field (figure 2.1), the flux linking the coil will be an alternating quantity, and an alternating EMF will be induced in the coil. In figure 2.1 connection is made to the coil by brushes bearing on sliprings; an alternating voltage is developed at the terminals (figure 2.2) which reverses with every half revolution of the coil. Suppose that instead of being connected to separate rings, the two ends of the coil are connected to the two parts of a divided ring (figure 2.3); this reverses the connections to the

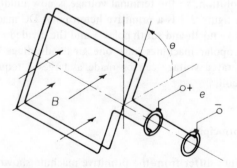

Figure 2.1   Elementary AC machine

45

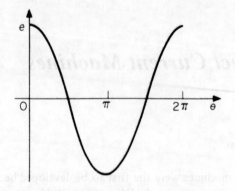

Figure 2.2 Generated EMF for the elementary AC machine

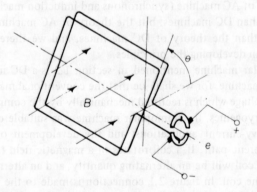

Figure 2.3 Elementary DC machine

coil every half revolution, so the terminal voltage is now unidirectional (figure 2.4). The device in figure 2.3 is a primitive heteropolar DC machine – the coils move under successive north and south poles – and the divided ring is a primitive commutator. Heteropolar machines have one great advantage over homopolar machines: the generated voltage can be made as large as required by winding more turns on the coil.

2.2 Fundamental principles

Practical DC machines differ from the primitive machine shown in figure 2.3 in one important respect: the active (armature) coils are wound on an iron cylinder, in order to reduce the length of the airgap in the magnetic circuit. The magnetic

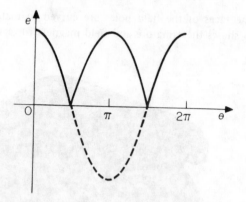

Figure 2.4   Generated EMF for the elementary DC machine

field is produced either by coils wound on iron poles or by permanent magnets; a small airgap will reduce the MMF – and hence the coil current or the magnet volume – required for a given flux density. Figure 2.5 shows the construction of a small wound-field machine; the armature coils are placed in slots in a cylindrical

Figure 2.5 Construction of a small wound–field DC machine (GEC Alsthom Electromotors Ltd)

iron core, and the faces of the field poles are curved to match the armature shape. Figure 2.6 shows the armature and field magnets for a small permanent-magnet machine.

Figure 2.6 Armature and field magnets for a small permanent–magnet DC machine (GEC Alsthom Electromotors Ltd)

The simplest approach to the principles of the DC machine is through an idealised model, shown in figure 2.7, which has a single-turn armature coil

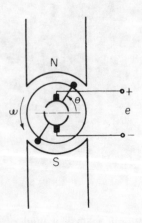

Figure 2.7 Simple DC machine

wound on the surface of a smooth iron cylinder. This model will be analysed to obtain the fundamental machine equations, and it will be shown that the equations also hold for the practical machine.

Voltage and torque equations for a simple model

Take the model shown in figure 2.7; assume that the magnetic field in the airgap is purely radial, and uniform along the length of the armature. The flux density B will, of course, vary with the angular position round the airgap, as shown in figure 2.8. Only the coil sides in the airgap will be considered; assume that the magnetic field outside the gap is negligible, so that the rest of the coil contributes nothing to the EMF or the torque.

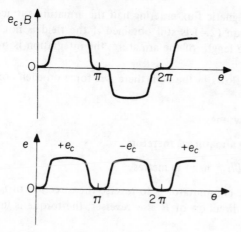

Figure 2.8   Flux density and generated EMF for the simple DC machine

As the armature rotates, the coil sides move in a magnetic field; an EMF will be generated in each conductor, given by eqn (1.5)

$$e = Blu \text{ volts}$$

The EMF developed in the whole coil is therefore

$$e_c = 2Blu = 2Blr\omega \text{ volts} \tag{2.1}$$

where l is the length of the armature in metres, r is the radius in metres and ω is the angular velocity in radians/second. The induced EMF thus varies with the angular position of the coil in the same way as the flux density, as shown in figure 2.8. The action of the commutator is to invert the negative half cycles of the coil EMF, so the terminal voltage is given by

$$e = 2\omega lr |B(\theta)| \tag{2.2}$$

as shown in figure 2.8. This is the instantaneous voltage, and the average value is

$$e_{av} = \frac{1}{\pi} \int_0^\pi e \, d\theta = \frac{1}{\pi} \int_0^\pi 2\omega lrB \, d\theta \qquad (2.3)$$

Now $lr \, d\theta = da$, an element of area of the armature surface. Equation (2.3) therefore becomes

$$e_{av} = \frac{2}{\pi} \omega \int_0^\pi Blr \, d\theta = \frac{2}{\pi} \omega \int_{\theta=0}^{\theta=\pi} B \, da$$

$$= \frac{2}{\pi} \Phi\omega \text{ volts} \qquad (2.4)$$

where Φ is the magnetic flux entering half the armature surface from one field pole. Note that eqn (2.4) is still obtained if the field is not purely radial or uniform along the length of the armature; the integration is simply more complicated.

If a current i_c flows in the coil, there is a force on each conductor given by eqn (1.14)

$$F = Bli_c \text{ newtons}$$

The torque on the armature is therefore

$$T = 2Fr = 2Bli_c r \text{ newton metres} \qquad (2.5)$$

The action of the commutator is to reverse the direction of i_c every half revolution; since the direction of B also reverses, the torque is unidirectional, and may be written as

$$T = 2ilr \, | \, B(\theta) \, | \qquad (2.6)$$

where i is the current in the armature circuit. The average torque is therefore

$$T_{av} = \frac{1}{\pi} \int_0^\pi 2ilB \, d\theta$$

$$= \frac{2}{\pi} \Phi i \text{ newton metres} \qquad (2.7)$$

Armature windings and commutator

The generated voltage of the simple DC machine is unidirectional, but far from constant. The performance can be improved by adding more conductors and commutator segments. Consider the effect of a second coil at right angles to the first (figure 2.9). The coil induced-EMF waveforms are shown in figure 2.10, together with the EMF e appearing at the terminals. There is an improvement in the output waveform, but each coil is now used for only half the time.

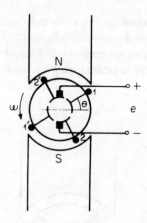

Figure 2.9 DC machine with two armature coils

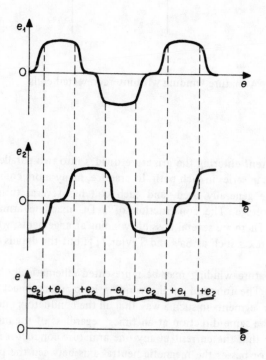

Figure 2.10 Generated EMF for the two-coil machine

In practical armature windings the coils and commutator segments are inter-connected so that the conductors carry current all the time, and there are usually several coils in series between the brushes. Figure 2.11 shows how four coils and four commutator segments may be used to achieve this result; note

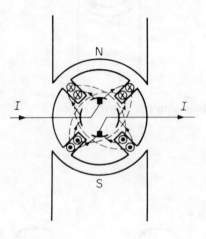

Figure 2.11   Armature winding with interconnected coils

that the current entering the armature divides into two parallel paths, and there are two coils in series in each path. In practice, many more coils and commutator segments are generally used, and each coil has several turns to increase the generated voltage. The construction of a DC machine armature is shown in figure 2.12. There are several possible winding arrangements, which are described in standard texts such as Say and Taylor [1]; but the details do not concern us here.

Any armature winding may be represented schematically by the diagram of figure 2.13. The function of the winding is to interconnect the coils and the commutator segments in such a way that all the conductors under one pole carry current in the same direction at all times, regardless of the motion of the armature. Notice that the current in any one armature conductor must reverse when the conductor passes the magnetic neutral axis between the poles. The currents in the armature coils are therefore alternating quantities, and the iron core of the armature is invariably laminated to reduce eddy current losses.

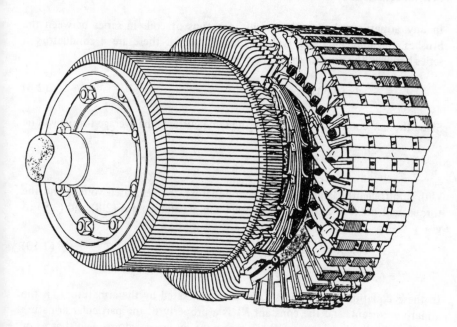

Figure 2.12 Construction of a DC machine armature (reproduced from *Electrical Machines* by A. Draper, Longman, 2nd edition, 1967)

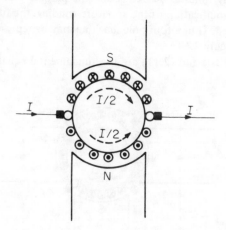

Figure 2.13 Schematic representation of a DC machine armature

General equations of the DC machine

In any armature winding there will be groups of coils in series between the brushes; the induced EMFs will be additive, and if there are n conductors in series between the brushes the average induced EMF will be

$$e_{av} = \frac{2n}{\pi} \Phi\omega \text{ volts} \tag{2.8}$$

Since these n conductors each carry the same current, the average torque will be

$$T_{av} = \frac{2n}{\pi} \Phi i \text{ newton metres} \tag{2.9}$$

With a sufficiently large number of conductors, the generated voltage and the torque will be very nearly constant; we can generalise eqns (2.8) and (2.9) to give

$$e_a = K_a\Phi\omega \text{ volts} \tag{2.10}$$

$$T = K_a\Phi i_a \text{ newton metres} \tag{2.11}$$

In these equations, e_a is the steady EMF generated by the armature; i_a is the armature current, and the constant K_a is a property of the particular armature winding. In the derivation of these equations we have not assumed that ω or i_a is a constant quantity, and they hold for transient as well as steady-state conditions.

More than two field poles may be employed, simply by repeating the N–S sequence as many times as desired round the periphery of the armature, with a corresponding modification of the armature winding; the fundamental principles remain unchanged. Thus a four-pole machine may be represented by the schematic diagram of figure 2.14.

Equations (2.10) and (2.11) are the fundamental equations of the machine,

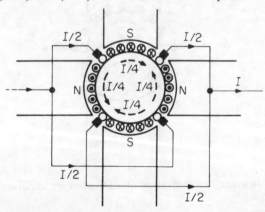

Figure 2.14 Four-pole DC machine

and we shall shortly deduce some of the interesting and useful characteristics of DC machines from them. Their simplicity is striking, and it conceals the inherent complexity of the commutation process. The action of a well-designed armature winding and commutator is to convert the alternating quantities in the armature coils into steady quantities at the brush terminals. The coils necessarily possess inductance, and the reversal of current in an inductive circuit is accompanied by an induced EMF or 'reactance voltage' which can cause sparking at the commutator. DC machines are therefore usually fitted with auxiliary poles (known as *interpoles*) to improve the commutation. These poles are placed midway between the main poles, and are wound with coils connected in series with the armature; their function is to induce an EMF which opposes the reactance voltage in the armature coils undergoing commutation. Interpoles do not affect the fundamental eqns (2.10) and (2.11), and they will not be considered further.

Field system and magnetisation curve

In permanent-magnet machines the field flux Φ is constant for normal operation, and there is nothing to add to eqns (2.10) and (2.11). But in wound-field machines it is necessary to consider how the pole flux is produced. Figure 2.15 is a schematic diagram of the structure of a wound-field DC machine without interpoles; the coils wound on the field poles are termed the *field* or *excitation winding* of

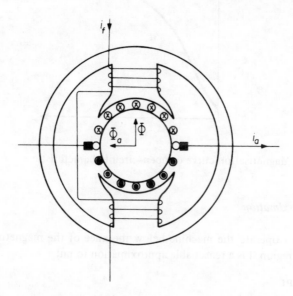

Figure 2.15 Wound–field DC machine

the machine. A current i_f flowing in the field winding will produce a pole flux Φ, as shown. With no armature current flowing, Φ will be a function of i_f only, and we may put $\Phi = \Phi(i_f)$; a graph of Φ against i_f (or $N_f i_f$, the field MMF) is known as the *magnetisation curve* of the machine. At constant speed, eqn (2.10) gives $e_a \propto \Phi$; a graph of e_a against i_f for zero armature current is known as the *open-circuit characteristic* of the machine, and this has the same shape as the magnetisation curve. Figure 2.16 shows a typical curve, and it will be seen that the middle portion is practically linear. In this region the iron is unsaturated, and the airgap reluctance is dominant in the magnetic circuit. The reluctance of the iron path increases rapidly with saturation, and this explains the shape of the curve for high values of field current. There is usually some remanent magnetisation of the iron, which accounts for the departure from linearity at low values of field current. Figure 2.16 is actually an over-simplification, for the magnetic circuit exhibits hysteresis; the curve for decreasing excitation will be slightly different from the curve for increasing excitation. The open-circuit characteristic may be regarded as the mean of the two curves.

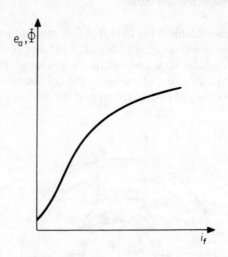

Figure 2.16 Magnetisation curve or open–circuit characteristic

Linear approximation

It is usual to operate the machine below the knee of the magnetisation curve, and for this region it is a reasonable approximation to put

$$\Phi = K_f i_f \tag{2.12}$$

The fundamental equations for this linear model then become

$$e_a = K i_f \omega \text{ volts} \tag{2.13}$$

$$T = Ki_f i_a \text{ newton metres} \tag{2.14}$$

where $K = K_a K_f$. These are the equations normally used in the analysis of systems containing DC machines.

Armature reaction

A current i_a flowing in the armature will produce a flux Φ_a, at right angles to Φ; this is known as the *armature reaction flux*, and by itself it will produce no torque or EMF. If the magnetic circuit were linear, there would be no interaction between Φ and Φ_a; in practice, Φ_a may cause local saturation of the magnetic circuit, and this will reduce the value of Φ for a given field current i_f. Thus $\Phi = \Phi(i_f, i_a)$, and in some applications this non-linear dependence of Φ on i_f and i_a must be considered. It is often sufficient, however, to ignore the effect of armature reaction and to take eqns (2.13) and (2.14) as the basic machine equations. The armature reaction flux can adversely affect the commutation, especially when the armature current changes rapidly. To overcome this difficulty, DC machines are sometimes fitted with compensating windings. These take the form of conductors embedded in slots in the field pole faces; they are connected in series with the armature, but carry current in the opposite direction so as to cancel the armature reaction flux.

DC machine action in terms of magnetic forces

The concept of armature reaction suggests an alternative physical picture for the mechanism of torque production in the DC machine. The existence of an armature reaction flux implies magnetisation of the armature iron, which may be represented by N and S poles, and the resultant magnetic field produced by the armature and field poles is shown in figure 2.17. From the Maxwell stress concept (or the properties of magnetic poles) it follows that there will be a torque on the armature tending to rotate its poles into alignment with the field poles. The armature winding and commutator, however, ensure that the magnetic axis of the armature remains fixed in space while the armature material revolves; a steady torque is therefore developed, which is unaffected by the rotation of the armature.

Slotted armature

In practice, as will be seen from figure 2.12, the armature conductors are placed in slots in the armature core. This profoundly alters the electromagnetic action of the machine, for the magnetic field in a slot is relatively weak (see figure 1.33) and the force on a conductor is reduced in consequence. It may be shown [2, 3] that the reduction in the conductor force is exactly compensated by

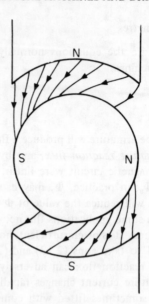

Figure 2.17   Magnetic field in a DC machine

forces acting on the slotted iron structure of the armature; the total torque is
still given by eqn (2.11). A qualitative explanation is that the magnetic field
pattern around the armature (figure 2.17) is, on average, the same whether or
not the conductors are placed in slots, and the torque produced by the Maxwell
stress will therefore be unchanged.

The EMF generated by the machine is still given by eqn (2.10), as may be
seen by applying Faraday's law to an armature coil; the change of flux through
the coil during one revolution of the armature is the same regardless of whether
the coil sides are in slots or on the surface. The flux cutting rule $e = Blu$ will give
different results if the field in the vicinity of the conductor is used for B; but
the dangers inherent in the use of this rule have already been mentioned (see
section 1.3).

An important principle is thus established: the basic machine equations are
the same for a slotted armature as for a smooth cylindrical armature, provided
that the total pole flux Φ (and hence the average value of B in the airgap) is
unchanged. This result will be used in later chapters to simplify the analysis of
AC machines.

2.3 Energy conversion and losses

Generators convert energy from mechanical to electrical form; motors perform
the inverse operation, and the efficiency of energy conversion is often an import-

ant consideration. Since the efficiency is directly related to the energy loss in the machine, the sources of loss are matters of considerable importance to the machine designer. The machine user also needs to be aware of these losses, and it is useful to discuss them briefly before examining the other characteristics of DC machines.

Generators and motors: sign conventions

A DC machine with its armature connected to a steady voltage source V_a is shown symbolically in figure 2.18. The armature circuit (conductors, commutator and brushes) will have a resistance represented by R_a, and the field

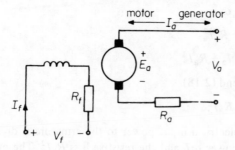

Figure 2.18   DC machine: circuit convention

winding will have a resistance R_f. If the steady generated voltage E_a is less than V_a, the source will supply power to the machine, which therefore acts as a motor. If we choose the direction of current flow so that the armature current I_a is positive under these conditions, then

$$V_a = E_a + R_a I_a \tag{2.15}$$

If $E_a > V_a$, the source will absorb power from the machine, which therefore acts as a generator. With the opposite direction for positive I_a, we now have

$$E_a = V_a + R_a I_a \tag{2.16}$$

Generator and motor action differ only in the directions of current and torque, and we adopt the convention that both the torque and the armature current will be positive when the machine is operating as a motor. The correct armature voltage equation is therefore eqn (2.15), not eqn (2.16); negative values of I_a and T will indicate that the machine is operating as a generator.

Losses and efficiency

The losses in a DC machine are essentially the same whether the machine operates as a generator or a motor, and motoring operation will be assumed for the rest of this section. Consider a DC machine with its armature connected to a voltage source V_a as shown in figure 2.18. With steady-state conditions the basic machine equations are

$$E_a = K_a \Phi \omega \qquad [2.10]$$

$$T = K_a \Phi I_a \qquad [2.11]$$

and we also have the motor armature equation

$$V_a = E_a + R_a I_a \qquad [2.15]$$

Multiplication of eqn (2.11) by ω, and eqns (2.10) and (2.15) by I_a, gives

$$\omega T = K_a \Phi I_a \omega \qquad (2.17)$$

$$V_a I_a = E_a I_a + R_a I_a^2$$
$$= K_a \Phi \omega I_a + R_a I_a^2 \qquad (2.18)$$

From eqns (2.17) and (2.18)

$$V_a I_a = \omega T + R_a I_a^2 \qquad (2.19)$$

showing that the electrical input power to the armature is divided between the gross mechanical power ωT and the resistive loss $R_a I_a^2$. The mechanical output from the motor shaft will be less than ωT, because some of the torque T (known as the *gross*, or *electromagnetic*, *torque*) will be absorbed in rotational losses. The flow of energy through the machine may be traced as follows

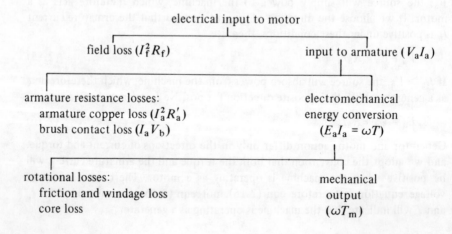

electrical input to motor

field loss ($I_f^2 R_f$)   input to armature ($V_a I_a$)

armature resistance losses: electromechanical
   armature copper loss ($I_a^2 R_a'$)   energy conversion
   brush contact loss ($I_a V_b$)   ($E_a I_a = \omega T$)

rotational losses: mechanical
   friction and windage loss   output
   core loss   (ωT_m)

Components of loss

The losses in the machine comprise the field and armature resistance losses and the rotational losses. Although the armature resistance loss is usually represented by the expression $R_a^2 I_a$, it should strictly be separated into the two components shown above because the brush contact resistance is non-linear. The voltage drop between the brushes and the commutator segments has an approximately constant value V_b over a wide range of currents, with a typical value of 2 volts for a pair of normal carbon brushes.

The two components of rotational loss are quite different in character. 'Friction and windage' accounts for all the mechanical and aerodynamic losses associated with the rotation of the armature, and varies roughly as the square of the speed. 'Core loss' includes the eddy-current and hysteresis loss in the laminated iron armature core, together with a similar surface loss in the field poles. The latter is a consequence of placing the armature conductors in slots; as the slots move past the field poles, the resulting local variations in the magnetic flux density produce eddy-current and hysteresis losses on the pole faces. A laminated construction is often used to minimise the eddy-current component of pole-face loss. The total core loss varies in a complex way with the speed, armature current and field flux.

Efficiency

An important property of an electrical machine is its efficiency under specified operating conditions. The efficiency η is defined in the usual way as

$$\eta = \frac{\text{output power}}{\text{input power}} \qquad (2.20)$$

$$= \frac{\text{input power} - \text{losses}}{\text{input power}}$$

$$= 1 - \frac{\text{losses}}{\text{input power}} \qquad (2.21)$$

Because of the difficulty of measuring input and output power accurately, the direct evaluation of efficiency implied by eqn (2.20) is seldom used; instead the losses are determined (usually from a number of different tests) and the efficiency is calculated from eqn (2.21).

2.4 DC generators

As sources of DC power, DC generators have been largely replaced by controlled semiconductor rectifiers, and a detailed treatment of their characteristics would be out of place in this book. Three types of generator, however, are worthy of mention: the permanent-magnet generator; the separately excited generator, in which the field winding is supplied from a separate power source; and the shunt generator or dynamo, which supplies its own excitation power.

Permanent-magnet generator

In a permanent-magnet DC machine the field flux Φ is substantially constant, and eqn (2.10) shows that the generated voltage e_a is directly proportional to the speed ω. Small machines of this kind, known as *tachogenerators*, are built specifically for speed measurement, and are widely used in feedback control systems. They require careful design to ensure that the field flux does not change with temperature or time.

Separately excited generator

When a wound-field DC machine is used as a source of power it is driven at a constant speed ω, and the field winding is connected to a voltage source V_f (figure 2.18). There will be a constant flux Φ, and the armature generated voltage has a constant value E_a given by eqn (2.10). With no load connected to the armature terminals, $V_a = E_a$; thus

$$V_a = K_a \omega \Phi \qquad (2.22)$$

The relationship between the open-circuit terminal voltage V_a and the field current I_f is given by the open-circuit characteristic (figure 2.16). In the linear region of the characteristic we may put

$$V_a = E_a \approx K \omega I_f = \frac{K \omega}{R_f} V_f \qquad (2.23)$$

showing that the output voltage is approximately proportional to the input voltage or current. The excitation power $V_f I_f$ is only a few per cent of the output power $V_a I_a$ when the machine is connected to a load; a DC generator may be regarded as a power amplifier, and has been widely used as such in control schemes such as the Ward–Leonard system [1].

Shunt generator

Instead of being connected to a separate voltage source, the field winding of a shunt generator is connected in parallel with the armature, so that the armature itself supplies the excitation current (figure 2.19). Frequently there is a variable resistor in series with the field, and total resistance will be denoted by R_f.

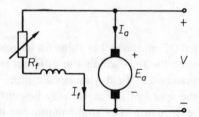

Figure 2.19   Shunt generator or motor

The operation of a shunt generator may be understood by drawing on the open-circuit characteristic of the machine a straight line representing the voltage/current characteristics of the resistance R_f (figure 2.20). The point at which this line intersects the open-circuit curve gives the no-load terminal voltage of the

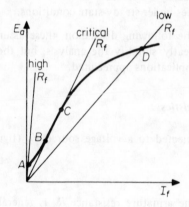

Figure 2.20   Operation of the shunt generator

machine, for the current flowing in the resistance is then just equal to the field current required to maintain that value of terminal voltage. When the resistance is high, the line intersects the curve at a point such as A, and the armature voltage is very small. As the value of R_f is reduced, the point of intersection moves up the curve until a critical value of R_f is reached; for lower values of R_f the operating point is at a position such as D in the saturation region. When R_f is equal to the critical value the generator is unstable, and very small changes in conditions can move the operating point from B to C. Shunt generators are normally designed to work well into the saturation region, so that the operating point is stable and the output voltage substantially constant.

2.5 DC motors

The great virtue of the DC motor is that three useful operating characteristics may be obtained by using the field winding in different ways. In the separately excited motor the armature and field windings are supplied from independent voltage sources, and the speed of the motor may be controlled by varying the voltage applied to the armature. The shunt motor has its field connected in parallel with the armature; this gives an almost constant speed, independent of voltage, over a wide range of loads. The series motor has its field connected in series with the armature, and this gives a characteristic in which the speed is inversely related to the torque load on the motor.

The essential features of DC motor performance may be deduced fairly readily if the following idealising assumptions are made

(a) the armature resistance R_a is neglected
(b) rotational losses are neglected
(c) magnetic non-linearity is ignored
(d) the motor operates under steady-state conditions.

As will be seen in the following discussion, these assumptions are not always appropriate; they greatly simplify the analysis, but their use must always be recognised and the implications appreciated.

Ideal motor characteristics

With the motor connected to a voltage source V_a (figure 2.18) the armature circuit equation is

$$V_a = E_a + R_a I_a \qquad\qquad [2.15]$$

The power loss in the armature resistance R_a is generally small in comparison with the input power to the motor, at least for machines with power ratings above 1 kW. It follows that the voltage drop $I_a R_a$ is usually small in comparison with V_a, and eqn (2.15) may be written as

$$V_a \approx E_a \qquad\qquad (2.24)$$

In the steady state, therefore, the operating conditions of the machine are determined by the fact that the generated EMF (or *back EMF*, as it is usually termed in a motor) must be approximately equal to the armature supply voltage. Since the back EMF E_a is related to the speed and field flux by the equation

$$E_a = K_a \Phi \omega \qquad\qquad [2.10]$$

then

$$V_a \approx K_a \Phi \omega$$

or

$$\omega \approx \frac{V_a}{K_a \Phi} \tag{2.25}$$

This equation is the basis of motor speed control, for it shows that the speed varies directly with the supply voltage V_a and inversely with the flux Φ. The other quantity of interest is the torque given by

$$T = K_a \Phi I_a \tag{2.11}$$

If we idealise the machine by putting $\Phi = (K/K_a)I_f$, these equations become

$$\omega \approx \frac{V_a}{K I_f} \tag{2.26}$$

$$T = K I_f I_a \tag{2.27}$$

Various methods of connecting the machine impose constraints between V_a, I_f and I_a, and we now explore some of the characteristics that may be obtained in this way.

Separately excited motor

With separate excitation (figure 2.18), I_f and V_a are controlled independently; the speed is given explicitly by eqn (2.26) and the torque by eqn (2.27). A motor is usually designed for a certain nominal speed at nominal values of armature voltage and field current; we examine the effect on the speed of varying the field current I_f and the armature voltage V_a from these nominal values.

Consider first the effect of varying the field current I_f. The normal value of field current will usually take the iron near to magnetic saturation. If the current I_f is increased above its normal value, saturation occurs; there is no longer a linear relationship between Φ and I_f, and eqn (2.26) is not valid. Equation (2.25) shows that the speed varies inversely with the flux Φ, and the flux cannot change appreciably once the iron is saturated. Thus speed control is possible only if the field current is reduced below its normal value – a process known as *field weakening*. This causes the motor speed to rise above its nominal value, as shown by eqn (2.26). The speed range obtainable by field weakening is rather restricted, for I_f cannot be reduced without limit. Equation (2.27) shows that the armature current I_a must increase inversely with I_f to maintain the torque, and commutation difficulties arise when the armature current is large and the field flux small.

Since field control can raise the speed only above the nominal value, armature voltage control must be used for speeds below the nominal value. Equations (2.25) and (2.26) show that the speed is nearly proportional to the armature voltage (for a constant field current), and a very wide speed range may be obtained by varying V_a. This linear relationship between speed and voltage is an important characteristic of the DC machine, which gives it a dominant position in speed control systems (both manual and automatic), with sizes ranging from a few watts to tens of megawatts. Field current and armature voltage control are often combined in applications which require exceptionally large speed ranges. DC drive systems, described in chapter 7, use power electronics to implement this method of speed control.

The effects of the armature resistance R_a can be included by using eqn (2.15) instead of eqn (2.24). The result is

$$\omega = \omega_0 (1 - T/T_0) \tag{2.28}$$

where ω_0 is the *no-load speed* given by

$$\omega_0 = V_a/(K_a \Phi) \tag{2.29}$$

and T_0 is the *stall torque* corresponding to the *stall armature current* I_{a0} at zero speed:

$$T_0 = K_a \Phi I_{a0} \tag{2.30}$$

$$I_{a0} = V_a/R_a \tag{2.31}$$

The resulting torque/speed characteristic is shown in figure 2.21. Two points should be noted about this characteristic and eqns (2.28) to (2.31). First, they are applicable only to small motors with power ratings below about 1 kW, where the voltage drop in R_a is significant. With large machines, the resistive term is small and armature reaction causes the speed to rise with increasing load because the pole flux is reduced. Secondly, the concepts of stall torque and stall current must be used with caution; it is unsafe actually to stall a motor with a power rating above a few hundred watts, because the low value of R_a would result in a damagingly large stall current.

Permanent-magnet motor

The permanent-magnet motor may be regarded as a separately excited motor with constant field flux. Its speed is nearly proportional to the armature supply voltage, and it has the advantage of higher efficiency because there is no energy loss in a field winding. The gain in efficiency can be significant for small motors. Laithwaite [4] has introduced a 'goodness factor' G for electromagnetic devices which gives a general measure of their performance; for similar devices, a larger value of G implies a higher efficiency. If all the linear dimensions of a device are multiplied by a factor x, then G will be multiplied by x^2. Thus electromagnetic devices get better as they get bigger, and conversely it is difficult to make a small motor with a high efficiency. The losses in the field and armature windings are often comparable in magnitude, so it is advantageous to replace the field winding with a permanent magnet in small motors. In large motors the field-winding loss is only a small fraction of the output power, and other factors such as material cost and manufacturing difficulty preclude the use of permanent magnets.

Shunt motor

In the shunt motor (figure 2.19) the field current I_f is obtained from the armature supply voltage V through a resistance R_f (internal winding resistance plus external variable resistance). Thus $I_f = V/R_f$, and eqns (2.26) and (2.27) become

$$T = \frac{K}{R_f} VI_f \tag{2.32}$$

$$\omega \approx \frac{R_f}{K} \tag{2.33}$$

Thus the speed is independent of V, and varies directly with R_f. Torque and speed are still independent, and the shunt motor is essentially a constant-speed machine. As with the separately excited machine, the range of speed variation obtainable by field weakening (increasing R_f) is limited, and the variable field resistance is normally used only for small variations from the nominal speed. If the effects of armature resistance are included, eqns (2.28) to (2.31) are applicable, with the no-load speed given by

$$\omega_0 = R_f/K \tag{2.34}$$

and the torque/speed curve as shown in figure 2.21.

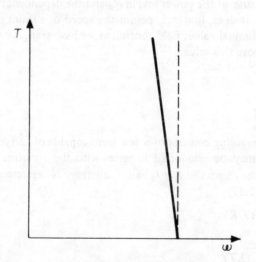

Figure 2.21 Torque/speed characteristic of a shunt motor

Some measure of speed control is possible by inserting additional resistance in series with the armature. Variation of this resistance gives a family of torque/speed curves, as shown in figure 2.22. If the torque/speed characteristic of the load is plotted on the same graph, its intersection with the motor torque/speed curve gives the speed at which the motor drives the load. The loaded speed of

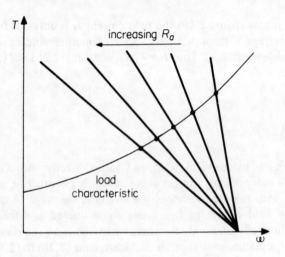

Figure 2.22   Speed control by armature resistance variation

the motor therefore falls with increasing R_a. This is not a good method of speed control, because of the power loss in R_a and the dependence of the speed on the load torque. It does, however, permit the speed of a shunt motor to be reduced below the nominal value; field control, as we have seen, is useful only for raising the speed above this value.

Series motor

If the field winding consists of a few turns capable of carrying the full armature current, it may be connected in series with the armature (figure 2.23). This introduces the constraint $I_f = I_a$ and if resistance is neglected we have, from eqns (2.25) and (2.27)

$$I = \sqrt{(T/K)} \tag{2.35}$$

$$\omega = \frac{V}{\sqrt{(KT)}} \tag{2.36}$$

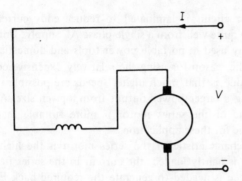

Figure 2.23 Series motor

Torque and speed are no longer independent, and the torque/speed characteristic is shown in figure 2.24. This is a useful characteristic for a vehicle traction motor; the machine develops high accelerating torque at low speeds, and as the speed rises the torque falls until it is just sufficient to maintain the speed of the vehicle. Series DC motors are used in battery electric vehicles and electric trains. Speed control of the series motor may be achieved by variation of the supply voltage V; eqn (2.36) shows that, for a given torque, the speed ω is directly proportional to V.

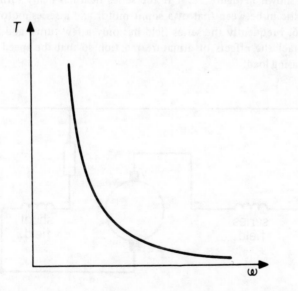

Figure 2.24 Torque/speed characteristic of the series motor

If the magnetic circuit is laminated to reduce eddy currents, a series DC motor will operate quite well from a single-phase AC supply. Universal motors of this kind are widely used in portable power tools and domestic appliances such as food mixers. The reason for using the relatively expensive construction of a commutator machine is that much higher speeds are possible than with induction motors, giving a larger power output from a given size. Also, the torque/speed characteristic of the series motor is more suitable than the induction motor characteristic for these applications.

An important characteristic of the series motor is the high speed attained when the machine is lightly loaded; the current in the series field is low, and a high rotational speed is needed to generate the required back EMF in the weak field flux. With a small machine the windage and friction torque is sufficient to limit the no-load speed to a safe value, but a large series motor must never be started without a load or the speed will rise to a very high value and the armature may burst under the rotational stresses. For this reason an auxiliary shunt winding is sometimes added to limit the no-load speed.

Compound motor

A DC motor is sometimes built with both shunt and series field windings connected as shown in figure 2.25. If the series field has many turns, this gives a characteristic in between that of a shunt motor and a series motor, as shown in figure 2.26. Frequently the series field has only a few turns, and its function is to counteract the effects of armature reaction so that the speed does not rise with increasing load.

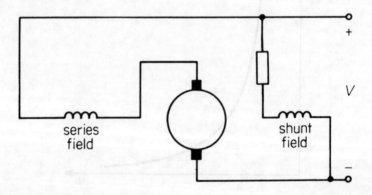

Figure 2.25   Compound motor

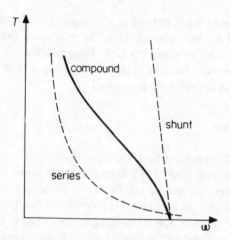

Figure 2.26 Torque/speed characteristic of the compound motor

Starting of DC motors

We have seen that the steady-state operation of DC motors is governed by the condition that the armature back EMF E_a is approximately equal to the supply voltage V_a. This condition does not hold when the motor is started from rest, for E_a is initially zero; if the armature were connected directly to the supply, a large stall current would flow, limited only by the armature resistance R_a. In fractional-kilowatt motors R_a is usually large enough to limit the starting current to a safe value, and such motors can be started by direct connection to the supply (direct-on-line or DOL starting). But large motors have a relatively small R_a, and a very large current would flow if the armature were connected directly to the full supply voltage. To prevent damage to the motor — particularly the commutator and brushes — the starting current must be limited. Electronic speed controllers normally incorporate a 'soft-start' facility to limit the starting current by control of the armature voltage. Large motors without electronic control are connected to the supply via a starter; this inserts a variable resistor in series with the armature, and the value of the resistor is progressively reduced as the armature runs up to speed.

The field current of a shunt or separately excited motor should always be set to its maximum value for starting, to give maximum starting torque with the available armature current and to give a rapid build-up of the back EMF as the armature accelerates. It is dangerous to attempt to start a motor with the field winding disconnected, because the residual flux may give enough torque to accelerate the armature, which will attain a dangerously high speed in order to generate the required back EMF. For the same reason, the field supply to a motor must never be disconnected while the machine is running; the armature supply must always be switched off first. These precautions do not, of course, apply to series motors, but the danger of starting a series motor without a mechanical load has already been mentioned.

2.6 Special machines

The majority of DC machines have the same basic form, regardless of size: the armature conductors lie in slots in a cylindrical iron rotor, and the field system – whether permanent magnet or otherwise – is stationary. DC machines which do not conform to this pattern have been developed for special purposes. Only the more common forms of special machine are described in this section; further information will be found in Say and Taylor [1], and constructional details in Kenjo and Nagamori [5]. Brushless DC motors are described in chapter 10.

Moving-coil machines

Motors and tachogenerators used in control systems are often required to have a very low rotor inertia so that the system can respond rapidly. With small machines this can be achieved by detaching the armature conductors from the iron core; the conductors are bonded in resin to form a 'basket' which is free to rotate in the airgap between the field poles and a fixed iron cylinder. Moving-coil motors of this kind generally develop a very smooth torque, since there are no rotor slots to cause 'cogging'. By the same token, moving-coil tachogenerators develop a smooth EMF. Low inertia is achieved at the expense of a large airgap, with a correspondingly large MMF to be supplied by the field windings or permanent magnets.

Disc machines

In a conventional DC machine, the magnetic field is radial and the current flow is axial; the two interact to give a circumferential force which exerts a torque on the cylindrical armature. A torque will also be produced if the directions of field and current are interchanged; this is the principle of the disc machine. An axial field is set up by permanent magnets, usually in opposing pairs. A disc-shaped armature, with conductors arranged radially like spokes, rotates in the axial magnetic field. The disc machine is thus a variant of the moving-coil machine, and it has similar properties. In addition it is very compact, and applications include drives for computer tape decks and engine cooling fans.

    The armature of a disc machine can be made from resin-bonded wire, as in the moving-coil machines. In small sizes another technique is widely used: conductors are formed on the surface of an insulated disc, either from punched metal sheet or by the methods used to make printed-circuit boards. For this reason disc motors are often called *printed-armature motors*. The construction of a typical printed-armature motor is shown in figure 2.27.

Linear DC motors

The disc machine is derived from the ordinary cylindrical machine by interchanging the directions of field and current; the force is still circumferential, giving rotary motion. Suppose that the radial field is retained, but the current direction is made circumferential; the force will then be axial, giving linear motion. This is the principle of the moving-coil loudspeaker mentioned in section 1.2, which may be regarded as a homopolar linear motor with very limited movement. A simple modification will allow much greater movement: the coil is wound on a long iron bar; current is supplied to a small section of this coil through brushes, and a radial magnetic field is applied to the energised section of the coil between the brushes [6]. As the bar moves, the brushes continually transfer the current to a new active section of the coil. Although the principle is simple, practical difficulties limit the usefulness of this type of machine. AC linear motors are more widely used than DC, and these are described in sections 5.4 and 6.7.

Problems

2.1. If the rotational losses of a DC shunt motor are constant, prove that the efficiency of the motor will be a maximum when the armature current is such that the armature resistance loss $I_a^2 R_a$ is equal to the sum of the rotational loss and the field resistance loss.

A 500 V DC shunt motor has a field winding resistance of 1000 Ω and a rated full-load output power of 10 kW. If the rotational losses amount to 250 W and the efficiency is a maximum at full load, calculate this efficiency and the value of the armature resistance.

2.2. If the field and armature windings of a DC machine carry alternating currents with RMS values I_f and I_a respectively, show that the average torque developed by the machine is given by

$$T = K I_f I_a \cos \phi$$

where ϕ is the phase angle between the currents and K is the machine constant.

A series motor is connected to an alternating voltage supply of RMS value V. Show that the average torque is given by

$$T = \frac{KV^2}{(R + K\omega_r)^2 + X^2}$$

where K is the machine constant, ω_r is the armature angular velocity, R is the total series resistance and X is the total series reactance of the windings at the frequency of the supply. Obtain the corresponding torque expression for the same motor operating from a DC supply and discuss the difference between AC and DC operation.

2.3. The hoisting cable of a crane is wound on to a drum, and a DC shunt motor drives the drum through a reduction gearbox. The crane is used to lift a load at a steady speed, and the speed is controlled by varying a resistance R in series with the armature. The internal armature resistance may be neglected.

Show that the hoisting speed u is given by the expression

$$u = u_0 - A W R$$

where u_0 is the no-load speed, W is the weight of the load and A is a constant. Also show that the efficiency of the system is u/u_0. Rotational losses in the motor and the gearbox may be neglected, and the cable winds on to the drum at a constant radius.

2.4. A 200 V DC shunt motor has a no-load speed of 100 rad/s and its armature resistance is 1 Ω. Rotational losses are negligible. The motor drives a water pump, and the normal torque load on the motor is 40 N m. A fault in the water system causes the torque load on the motor to fall suddenly to 20 N m. Calculate

(a) the normal armature current
(b) the normal speed at which the motor drives the pump
(c) the motor armature current just after the fault has occurred
(d) the final armature current
(e) the final motor speed.

If the rotating parts have a moment of inertia of 0.1 kg m^2, and the inductance of the armature may be neglected, obtain the differential equation which governs the speed of the motor after the fault.

2.5. A separately excited DC motor has a constant field current I_f. When a voltage v is applied to the armature a current i will flow; if the motor is unloaded, the resulting torque will accelerate the armature. Neglecting rotational losses, show that

$$v = \frac{(KI_f)^2}{J} \int i \, dt + R_a i + L_a \frac{di}{dt}$$

where J is the moment of inertia and K is the machine constant. Hence show that the machine is equivalent to a series combination of resistance R_a, inductance L_a and capacitance $C_m = J/(KI_f)^2$. If a constant voltage V is applied for a sufficiently long time, the current will be zero and the energy stored in the capacitance will be $\frac{1}{2}C_m V^2$. Prove that this is equal to the rotational energy of the armature.

References

1 M. G. Say and E. O. Taylor, *Direct Current Machines*, 2nd ed. (London: Pitman, 1986).
2 G. W. Carter, *The Electromagnetic Field in its Engineering Aspects*, 2nd ed. (London: Longman, 1967).
3 B. Hague, *The Principles of Electromagnetism Applied to Electrical Machines* (New York: Dover, 1962).

76 ELECTRICAL MACHINES AND DRIVES

4 E. R. Laithwaite, 'The goodness of a machine', *Proc. IEE*, **112** (1965), pp. 538–41.

5 T. Kenjo and S. Nagamori, *Permanent-Magnet and Brushless DC Motors* (Oxford University Press, 1985).

6 G. W. McLean, 'Review of recent progress in linear motors', *IEE Proc. B. Electr. Power Appl.*, **135** (1988), pp. 380–416.

3 *Alternating Current Systems*

3.1 Introduction

With DC machines, the voltage generated by an individual armature coil is an alternating quantity which is rectified mechanically by the commutator. If we dispense with the commutator and revert to the slipring model of figure 2.1, we have a rudimentary AC generator. Practical AC generators are essentially simpler than their DC counterparts and are more easily designed in very large sizes; but a more important reason for their adoption is the possibility of using transformers to raise the voltage level for power transmission over long distances, and then to reduce it again for domestic or industrial consumption.

In nearly all applications, alternating current has advantages over direct current. The usefulness of the transformer is one reason, but it is the induction motor more than any other device which has vindicated the alternating current system. Induction motors are cheap, efficient and robust; they supply most of the motive power for industry, and they are used in many domestic appliances. The other main type of AC machine is the synchronous machine; most AC generators are of this kind, and in large sizes the synchronous motor is a strong rival to the induction motor. These machines are treated in chapters 4, 5 and 6, but it is first necessary to consider some of the general properties of AC systems; this is done in sections 3.2 and 3.3.

Transformers are considered in section 3.4. Although they have no moving parts they are traditionally included with electrical machines, for the theory of the transformer makes a useful introduction to the theory of AC rotating machines. The idea of an equivalent circuit, which arises naturally in the study of the transformer, proves to be a useful concept in rotating machines. Imperfections such as magnetic leakage and core loss are present in AC machines as well as transformers, and they can be represented by similar elements in the equivalent circuits.

3.2 Generation of sinusoidal alternating voltages

The EMF generated in a coil depends only on the rate of change of the flux linking the coil; it is of no consequence whether the coil moves in the field of fixed magnetic poles, or the poles move and the coil remains stationary. Usually,

77

it is more convenient to have the active coils stationary and field poles rotating, as shown in the simple model of figure 3.1. This is always done with large machines, to avoid the transfer of large amounts of power through sliprings. In the simple model, the rotor is magnetised by a field coil (or 'excitation winding'), with the field current supplied via brushes and sliprings (not shown in figure 3.1). The stationary part of the machine (the 'stator') carries a single-turn armature coil, and an EMF will be induced in this coil when the rotor moves. If the rotor angular velocity is ω, the induced EMF, which has already been calculated for the DC machine, is

$$e = 2Blr\omega \qquad\qquad [2.1]$$

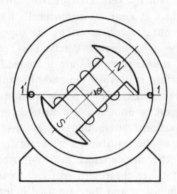

Figure 3.1   Simple single–phase AC generator

where l is the length of a coil side and r is the radius. The flux density B is the value at the right-hand coil side, which is displaced by an angle θ from the magnetic axis of the rotor. During each revolution of the rotor B will vary with θ, and by suitably shaping the poles it can be arranged that

$$B = B_m \cos \theta \qquad\qquad (3.1)$$

If θ has some value θ_0 at time $t = 0$, and the angular velocity ω is constant, then $\theta = \omega t + \theta_0$ and eqn (3.1) becomes

$$B = B_m \cos (\omega t + \theta_0) \qquad\qquad (3.2)$$

The induced EMF is now a sinusoidal alternating quantity, given by

$$e = 2lr\omega B_m \cos (\omega t + \theta_0)$$

$$= E_m \cos (\omega t + \theta_0) \qquad\qquad (3.3)$$

where $E_m = 2lr\omega B_m$. Strictly speaking this is a cosinusoidal quantity; but the term 'sinusoidal' will be used to describe a sine or a cosine function. Sine waves are distinguished from all other periodic functions by the fact that the steady-state response of any linear electric circuit to a sine wave of voltage is also sinusoidal. It is therefore advantageous to generate alternating voltages in the form of sine waves for general transmission and distribution, and generators are normally designed to do this. As with DC machines, practical AC generators differ from the simple model in having many armature coils; these machines are considered in chapter 4.

3.3 Polyphase systems

Suppose that a second armature coil is added to the simple generator, at right angles to the first, as shown in figure 3.2. If the flux density at coil side α is

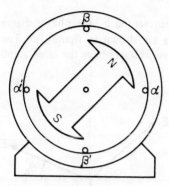

Figure 3.2   Simple two-phase AC generator

$B_m \cos \theta$, the corresponding value at coil side β is $B_m \cos (\theta - \pi/2)$. The generated voltages are then given by

$$e_\alpha = E_m \cos (\omega t + \theta_0)$$
$$e_\beta = E_m \cos (\omega t + \theta_0 - \pi/2)$$

(3.4)

These voltages have the same frequency but different phase angles; the two armature coils are known as *phases*, and the voltages are the *phase voltages*. This two-phase system is a rather special case, and the general symmetrical m-phase (or polyphase) system is obtained from m coils arranged symmetrically round the armature. Thus for a three-phase generator (figure 3.3) we have

$$e_a = E_m \cos (\omega t + \theta_0)$$
$$e_b = E_m \cos (\omega t + \theta_0 - 2\pi/3)$$
$$e_c = E_m \cos (\omega t + \theta_0 - 4\pi/3)$$

(3.5)

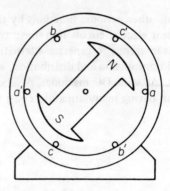

Figure 3.3 Simple three–phase AC generator

These voltages may be represented by the phasor diagram of figure 3.4, and the corresponding waveforms are shown in figure 3.5. The generator is said to be *balanced* when all the phase voltages have the same amplitude, as they do here.

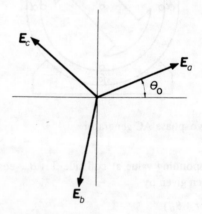

Figure 3.4 Phasor diagram for three–phase voltages

Three-phase systems

Most AC machines require balanced polyphase currents for satisfactory operation. (A notable exception is the small single-phase induction motor, discussed in section 6.6.) In principle any number of phases upwards of two could be used, with machines of appropriate design; in practice three phases are almost universally used for economic reasons. The economics of AC power transmission systems may be compared on the basis of the same maximum voltage between

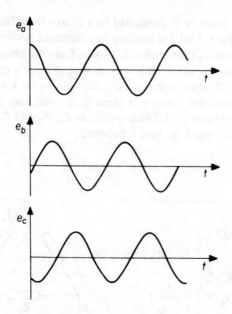

Figure 3.5 Waveforms for three–phase voltages

conductors and the same total I^2R loss in all the conductors; a three-phase system using three conductors requires less total conductor material than any other number of phases, including single phase [1].

The three armature coils of a three-phase generator may be represented in a circuit diagram by three voltage generators or sources. There are two ways in which these sources may be connected together so as to transmit power with fewer than six conductors. In the star or wye (Y) connection of figure 3.6(a), there is a choice of a three-wire or four-wire system, depending on whether the

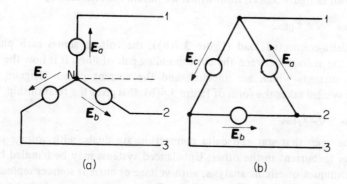

Figure 3.6 Connection of a three–phase source: (a) star, (b) delta

star (or neutral) point N is connected to a fourth line. The mesh or delta (Δ) connection of figure 3.6(b) is possible in a balanced system because $e_a + e_b + e_c = 0$ at all instants of time (this may be seen from the phasor diagram; the sum of the three phasors is zero). Only a three-wire system is possible with a delta-connected source. In each case the individual sources are known as *phases*. If we consider only three-wire systems, a three-phase load may be connected to the lines in two ways (figure 3.7). The impedances Z_a, Z_b and Z_c form the phases of the load; if they are equal the load is balanced.

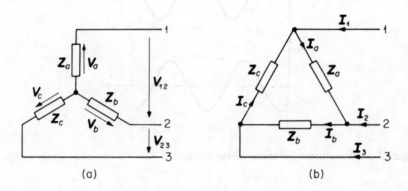

Figure 3.7   Connection of a three–phase load: (a) star, (b) delta

When the load is star connected (figure 3.7(a)), the current in each phase of the load is equal to the current in the corresponding line. The voltage across a phase, however, is not equal to the voltage between a pair of lines. When the source and load are balanced, the voltage phasor diagram takes the symmetrical form shown in figure 3.8(a), from which we obtain the relationship

$$V_{\text{line}} = \sqrt{3}\ V_{\text{phase}} \tag{3.6}$$

With a delta-connected load (figure 3.7(b)), the voltage across each phase is equal to the voltage between the corresponding pair of lines. It is now the phase and line currents which are unequal, and the current phasor diagram for a balanced system takes the form of figure 3.8(b); this gives the relationship

$$I_{\text{line}} = \sqrt{3}\ I_{\text{phase}} \tag{3.7}$$

It will be seen that star and delta connection are duals, with voltage in one analogous to current in the other. Unbalanced systems may be handled by the usual techniques of circuit analysis, with voltage or current sources representing the phases of the generator. The star–delta (T–π) transformation of circuit theory is often useful for converting star loads to equivalent delta form, and vice versa.

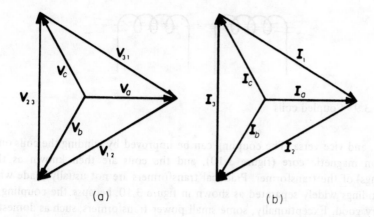

(a)   (b)

Figure 3.8   Phasor diagrams for a balanced load: (a) star, (b) delta

When the load is balanced, the relationship between the phase impedances for equivalent star and delta configurations is

$$Z_{\text{delta}} = 3Z_{\text{star}} \tag{3.8}$$

Phase sequence

In the three-phase system so far considered, the voltages pass through their maximum positive values in the sequence $a \rightarrow b \rightarrow c$. This is the normal arrangement, and it is termed the *positive phase sequence*. If any pair of phases is interchanged the sequence will be reversed; thus interchanging e_b and e_c will give the system

$$e_{a'} = e_a = E_m \cos(\omega t + \theta_0)$$

$$e_{b'} = e_c = E_m \cos(\omega t + \theta_0 - 4\pi/3) = E_m \cos(\omega t + \theta_0 + 2\pi/3)$$

$$e_{c'} = e_b = E_m \cos(\omega t + \theta_0 - 2\pi/3) = E_m \cos(\omega t + \theta_0 + 4\pi/3)$$

The phase sequence for this system is $c' \rightarrow b' \rightarrow a'$, which is termed the *negative sequence*. It will be shown in chapter 4 that the direction of rotation of an AC motor depends on the phase sequence of the supply, and a positive sequence is normally assumed.

3.4 Transformers

A transformer is a pair of coils coupled magnetically (figure 3.9), so that some of the magnetic flux produced by the current in the first coil links the turns of the

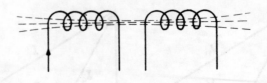

Figure 3.9   Coupled coils

second, and vice versa. The coupling can be improved by winding the coils on a common magnetic core (figure 3.10), and the coils are then known as the 'windings' of the transformer. Practical transformers are not usually made with the windings widely separated as shown in figure 3.10, because the coupling is not very good. Exceptionally, some small power transformers, such as domestic bell transformers, are sometimes made this way; the physical separation allows the coils to be well insulated for safety reasons. Figure 3.11 shows the shell type of construction which is widely used for single-phase transformers. The windings are placed on the centre limb either side-by-side or one over the other, and the magnetic circuit is completed by the two outer limbs. Say [2] gives details of different types of transformer construction and of three-phase transformers, which are beyond the scope of this book.

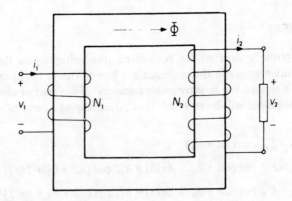

Figure 3.10 Elementary transformer

The ideal transformer

In an ideal transformer, the same core flux Φ links each turn of each winding. Suppose that one winding (known as the *primary*) is connected to a voltage source v_1; it will draw a current i_1, and the voltage equation is

$$v_1 = R_1 i_1 + N_1 \frac{d\Phi}{dt} \tag{3.9}$$

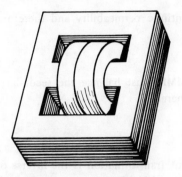

Figure 3.11   Shell-type transformer construction

If the other winding (known as the *secondary*) is connected to a load, a current i_2 will flow, and the terminal voltage v_2 is given by

$$v_2 = N_2 \frac{d\Phi}{dt} - R_2 i_2 \tag{3.10}$$

the negative sign arising from the different direction of current flow. If the windings have negligible resistance, then eqns (3.9) and (3.10) reduce to

$$v_1 = N_1 \frac{d\Phi}{dt} \tag{3.11}$$

$$v_2 = N_2 \frac{d\Phi}{dt} \tag{3.12}$$

and these are the fundamental voltage equations of the ideal transformer. By division

$$\frac{v_2}{v_1} = \frac{N_2}{N_1} = n \tag{3.13}$$

where n is the turns ratio.

To find a relationship between i_1 and i_2, consider the magnetic circuit of the core. If S is the reluctance, then

$$S\Phi = F = N_1 i_1 - N_2 i_2 \tag{3.14}$$

The reluctance of the core is given by

$$S = \frac{l}{\mu_0 \mu_r A} \tag{1.75}$$

and if the relative permeability μ_r is high, S will be small. In an ideal transformer we postulate infinite permeability and therefore zero reluctance; eqn (3.14) becomes

$$N_1 i_1 = N_2 i_2 \qquad (3.15)$$

that is, the primary MMF must balance the secondary MMF. The required current relationship is therefore

$$\frac{i_2}{i_1} = \frac{N_1}{N_2} = \frac{1}{n} \qquad (3.16)$$

showing that the current transformation is the inverse of the voltage transformation. Equations (3.13) and (3.16) may be rewritten in the form

$$v_2 = nv_1 \qquad (3.17)$$

$$i_2 = \frac{1}{n} i_1 \qquad (3.18)$$

Multiplication of eqn (3.17) by (3.18) gives

$$v_2 i_2 = v_1 i_1 \qquad (3.19)$$

showing that the instantaneous power output is equal to the instantaneous power input.

With steady AC conditions we have the phasor equations

$$V_2 = nV_1 \qquad (3.20)$$

$$I_2 = \frac{1}{n} I_1 \qquad (3.21)$$

If an impedance Z_2 is connected to the secondary (figure 3.12), then $V_2/V_1 = Z_2$. Division of eqn (3.20) by (3.21) gives

$$Z_2 = \frac{V_2}{I_2} = n^2 \frac{V_1}{I_1}$$

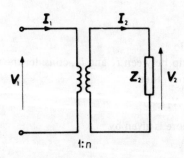

Figure 3.12 Ideal transformer with a load

Now V_1/I_1 is the impedance Z_1 presented by the primary terminals; hence

$$Z_1 = \frac{1}{n^2} Z_2 \qquad (3.22)$$

so the transformer has the property of changing impedances. It is this property which makes the transformer so useful in electronic and communication circuits; in power circuits it is the voltage or current transforming property which is of interest.

The real transformer

In a real (as opposed to an ideal) transformer, the winding resistances are not zero; the magnetic coupling between the coils is not perfect; and the reluctance of the core is not zero. We now show that it is possible to represent the real transformer by an equivalent circuit consisting of an ideal transformer together with other elements which represent the imperfections. Since the transformer is a pair of coupled coils, we may use the coupled circuit equations derived in section 1.3, with the notation of figure 3.13

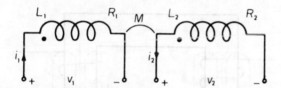

Figure 3.13   Coupled coils: notation

$$\left.\begin{array}{l} v_1 = R_1 i_1 + L_1 \dfrac{di_1}{dt} - M \dfrac{di_2}{dt} \\[2ex] v_2 = -R_2 i_2 - L_2 \dfrac{di_2}{dt} + M \dfrac{di_1}{dt} \end{array}\right\} \qquad (3.23)$$

The negative signs in these equations arise from the reversed direction of the secondary current i_2. The winding resistances occur explicitly in these equations but it is not obvious how the magnetic imperfections are included. It is necessary to rearrange the inductive terms in eqns (3.23) by introducing the concept of leakage inductance.

Leakage inductance

The reluctance of the magnetic circuit is finite, and the magnetic circuit law $NI = S\Phi$ implies that a current is required to set up the working flux in the transformer core. Thus if a current i_1 flows in the primary winding, with no current in the secondary, the flux linkage with the primary winding is given by

$$\psi_1 = L_1 i_1 \tag{3.24}$$

and the average flux per turn is

$$\Phi_1 = \frac{L_1 i_1}{N_1} \tag{3.25}$$

Some of the flux produced by the primary current will also link the secondary winding; the flux linkage is given by

$$\psi_{21} = M i_1 \tag{3.26}$$

and the average flux per turn for the secondary is

$$\Phi_{21} = \frac{M i_1}{N_2} \tag{3.27}$$

If the coupling were perfect the same flux would link each turn of each winding. On account of magnetic leakage (figure 3.14) the flux Φ_{21} linking the turns of

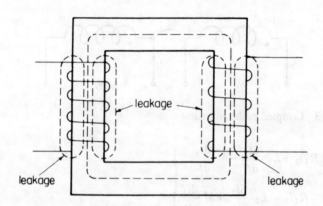

Figure 3.14 Leakage flux

the secondary will be less than the flux Φ_1 linking the primary, and we may define the leakage flux Φ_{l_1} as the difference between these quantities

$$\Phi_{l_1} = \Phi_1 - \Phi_{21} \tag{3.28}$$

Since Φ_1 and Φ_{21} are both proportional to the current i_1 we may put

$$\Phi_{l_1} = \frac{l_1 i_1}{N_1} \tag{3.29}$$

The quantity l_1 is termed the *leakage inductance* of the primary winding, and its physical interpretation is as follows: the flux produced by the current i_1 flowing in the inductance l_1 represents that portion of the primary flux which fails to link with the secondary.

The leakage inductance l_1 may be expressed in terms of L_1 and M, for we have

$$\Phi_{l_1} = \Phi_1 - \Phi_{21}$$

$$= \frac{L_1 i_1}{N_1} - \frac{M i_1}{N_2} \qquad [3.28]$$

and eqn (3.29) gives the result

$$l_1 = \frac{N_1 \Phi_{l_1}}{i_1} = L_1 - \frac{N_1}{N_2} M \qquad (3.30)$$

Similarly there is a secondary leakage flux given by

$$\Phi_{l_2} = \Phi_2 - \Phi_{12} = \frac{L_2 i_2}{N_2} - \frac{M i_2}{N_1} \qquad (3.31)$$

and a secondary leakage inductance

$$l_2 = L_2 - \frac{N_2}{N_1} M \qquad (3.32)$$

Equivalent circuit

The leakage inductances may be incorporated into the coupled circuit equations; from eqns (3.30) and (3.32) we have

$$L_1 = l_1 + \frac{N_1}{N_2} M$$

$$L_2 = l_2 + \frac{N_2}{N_1} M \qquad (3.33)$$

and eqns (3.23) become

$$\left. \begin{aligned} v_1 &= R_1 i_1 + l_1 \frac{di_1}{dt} + \frac{1}{n} M \frac{d}{dt}(i_1 - n i_2) \\[2mm] v_2 &= -R_2 i_2 - l_2 \frac{di_2}{dt} + M \frac{d}{dt}(i_1 - n i_2) \end{aligned} \right\} \qquad (3.34)$$

where $n = N_2/N_1$ as before. Equations (3.34) are the equations of the circuit shown in figure 3.15, which is the required equivalent circuit. This is a time-

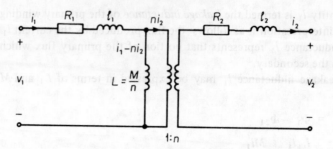

Figure 3.15 Time–domain equivalent circuit of the transformer

domain circuit, valid for arbitrarily time-varying voltages and currents, subject only to the assumptions made in deriving the equations. These are

(a) capacitance effects, between turns and between the two windings, are negligible
(b) magnetic non-linearity is ignored
(c) iron losses are ignored.

We now consider steady-state sinusoidal operation and the representation of iron losses.

AC equivalent circuit of the transformer

For sinusoidal AC operation we may draw an AC (frequency-domain) circuit corresponding to figure 3.15, with inductances replaced by reactances and instantaneous quantities replaced by phasor (complex) quantities. The AC circuit is shown in figure 3.16, in which an additional resistance R_c has been connected in parallel with the reactance jX_m. This resistance represents the iron loss in the core, and the reason for placing it in parallel with jX_m will be explained

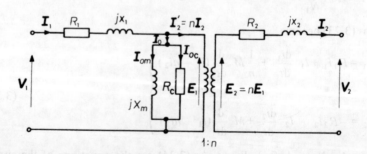

Figure 3.16 Frequency–domain equivalent circuit of the transformer

presently. Capacitance has again been neglected, so the circuit is valid only up to the low audio frequencies.

The equivalent circuit consists of an ideal transformer of ratio $1 : n = N_1 : N_2$, together with elements which represent the imperfections of the real transformer. The voltage E_1 across the primary of the ideal transformer represents the voltage induced in the primary winding by the mutal flux Φ. This is the portion of the core flux which links both primary and secondary coils; the leakage flux associated with one winding does not link the other, and it is represented in the circuit by the leakage reactances jx_1 and jx_2. Similarly, the voltage E_2 across the secondary of the ideal transformer represents the voltage induced in the secondary winding by the mutual flux Φ.

Voltage equation

From eqn (3.11) for the ideal transformer, we have

$$E_1 = j\omega N_1 \Phi \tag{3.35}$$

showing that the induced voltage is in quadrature with the mutual flux. If Φ_{max} is the peak value of the core flux, then the RMS magnitude of the primary voltage is

$$E_1 = \frac{\omega}{\sqrt{2}} N_1 \Phi_{max}$$

$$= 4.44 f N_1 \Phi_{max} \tag{3.36}$$

where f is the frequency of the supply. Equation (3.36) is a basic design equation for a transformer or an iron-cored inductor. The peak core flux is given by

$$\Phi_{max} = A B_{max} \tag{3.37}$$

where A is the cross-sectional area of the core and B_{max} is the peak flux density. The maximum value of B_{max} is set by saturation of the magnetic material, and this fixes the maximum value of Φ_{max} for a given device. Equation (3.36) shows that E_1 must vary in proportion to f if the magnitude of the flux is to remain constant; this is the basis of the 'constant volts per hertz' rule for variable-frequency operation of iron-cored devices.

Magnetising current

In the ideal transformer, the reluctance of the core is zero and there is an exact MMF balance between the primary and secondary. In the real transformer, on the other hand, the reluctance of the core is finite, and the primary MMF $N_1 I_1$ must exceed the secondary MMF $N_2 I_2$ by an amount required to set up the mutual flux Φ in the core. When the secondary current I_2 is zero, the primary current has a finite value I_0, known as the *no-load current*. This current has a component I_{0c}, in phase with E, to supply the eddy-current and hysteresis losses in the core; and a component I_{0m}, known as the *magnetising current*, to set up the core flux. The magnetising current is, of course, the current flowing in the inductive reactance of the primary winding. From figure 3.16 and eqn (3.35) we have

$$I_{0m} = \frac{E_1}{jX_m} = \frac{\omega N_1}{X_m}\Phi \qquad\qquad (3.38)$$

showing that the magnetising current I_{0m} is in phase with the mutual flux Φ.

Core loss

It only remains to justify the use of the resistance R_c to represent losses in the iron core. From eqns (3.36) and (3.37) we have

$$E_1 \propto f B_{max}$$

so the core loss is represented by

$$P_c = E_1^2/R_c \propto f^2 B_{max}^2$$

But from eqns (1.64) and (1.65) we also have

$$P_e \propto f^2 B_{max}^2$$

$$P_h \propto f B_{max}^{1.7}$$

where P_e is the eddy-current loss and P_h is the hysteresis loss. It follows that eddy-current loss can be represented by a constant resistance, but that hysteresis loss must be represented by a resistance which varies with f and B_{max}. Thus the value of R_c is independent of the frequency and voltage only if there is no hysteresis loss; since this is not the case, the correct value of R_c must be chosen for the particular operating conditions. With power transformers the frequency is fixed and E_1 does not vary by more than a few per cent when the primary supply voltage V_1 is held constant, so the variation in the value of R_c may be ignored.

Phasor diagram

When the secondary current I_2 is zero (the secondary is on open circuit) the primary current I_1 is just equal to I_0 — the total current flowing in the shunt elements R_c and jX_m. When a load is connected to the secondary, a current I_2 flows, and the primary current is increased by an amount $I_2' = nI_2$. This is termed the *load component* of the primary current, or the secondary current *referred* to the primary, and the total primary current is given by

$$I_1 = I_0 + nI_2 \qquad\qquad (3.39)$$

From the equivalent circuit, we also have

$$V_2 = E_2 - I_2(R_2 + jx_2)$$

$$= nV_1 - nI_1(R_1 + jx_1) - I_2(R_2 + jx_2) \qquad (3.40)$$

These and other relationships are conveniently illustrated by the phasor diagram of figure 3.17. Equations (3.39) and (3.30) reduce to the ideal transformer equations when both the no-load current I_0 is zero and the leakage impedances

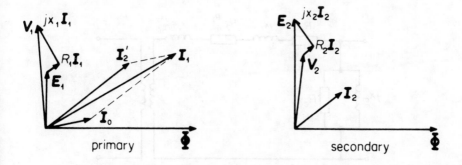

Figure 3.17 Phasor diagram for the transformer

$R_1 + jx_1$ and $R_2 + jx_2$ are zero.

Simplification of the equivalent circuit

Practical iron-cored transformers are usually designed so that under normal working conditions the volt drop in R_1 and x_1 is small in comparison with V_1, and I_0 is small in comparison with the load current I_1. The shunt components R_c and X_m may then be transferred to the input terminals with very little loss of accuracy (figure 3.18(a)). The secondary quantities R_2 and x_2 may be replaced by equivalent quantities on the primary side, using the impedance-transforming property of the ideal transformer, as shown in figure 3.18(b). The actual primary quantities R_1 and x_1 can then be combined with the referred secondary quantities R_2' and x_2' to give the equivalent primary quantities R_e and X_e (figure 3.18(c)). This is the normal form of the equivalent circuit for small power transformers; it simplifies the analysis because the current I_0 is determined solely by the applied primary voltage V_1, and the parameters are readily determined from simple tests. Figure 3.18 shows the elements referred to the primary side, and a 'mirror image' circuit is readily derived with all the elements referred to the secondary. This form is useful when the transformer is operated in an inverted

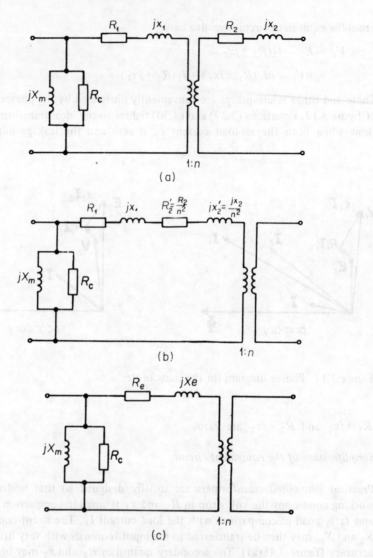

Figure 3.18 Simplified equivalent circuit of the transformer

mode, with a voltage applied to the secondary and a load connected to the primary.

Determination of the equivalent circuit parameters

The parameters of the approximate equivalent circuit are readily obtained from open-circuit and short-circuit tests, as follows.

In the open-circuit test one winding is left on open circuit and the normal voltage is applied to the other winding; only the small no-load current will be drawn from the supply. If the secondary is open-circuited the referred secondary current I_2' will be zero, and the equivalent circuit reduces to the form shown in figure 3.19. Measurements are made of the voltage V_0, the current I_0, and the

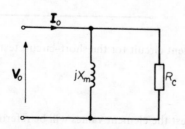

Figure 3.19 Equivalent circuit for the open–circuit test

input power P_0. The shunt elements X_m and R_c may then be determined from the relations

$$R_c = V_0^2/P_0 \qquad (3.41)$$

$$Y_0 = I_0/V_0 \qquad (3.42)$$

$$X_m = 1/\sqrt{(Y_0^2 - 1/R_c^2)} \qquad (3.43)$$

For the short-circuit test, one winding is short circuited and the normal full-load current is allowed to flow in the other winding by connecting it to an adjustable low-voltage source. Thus if the secondary is short circuited, a short circuit will be reflected into the primary side of the equivalent circuit. The leakage impedance is thus placed in parallel with the magnetising impedance; since these generally differ by at least two orders of magnitude the magnetising impedance may be ignored, and the equivalent circuit takes the form shown in figure 3.20. Measurements are made of the voltage V_{sc}, the current I_{sc} and the input power P_{sc}; the series elements are then determined from the relations

$$R_e = R_{sc}/I_{sc}^2 \qquad (3.44)$$

$$Z_e = V_{sc}/I_{sc} \qquad (3.45)$$

$$X_e = \sqrt{(Z_e^2 - R_e^2)} \qquad (3.46)$$

In practice the open-circuit measurements are usually made on the low-voltage side of the transformer and the short-circuit measurements on the high-voltage side (where the current will be lower). This is done merely for convenience, to avoid using higher voltages and currents than necessary; the same equations

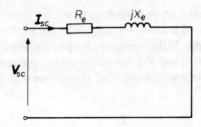

Figure 3.20   Equivalent circuit for the short–circuit test

apply, but for one test the element values will be referred to the primary and for
the other they will be referred to the secondary. Conversion of secondary values
to equivalent primary values (or vice versa) involves the turns ratio of the transformer; this is taken to be the primary–secondary voltage ratio measured in the
open-circuit test.

Regulation and efficiency

Because of the volt drop in the series impedances of the windings, the transformer secondary terminal voltage will vary with the load current. The *voltage
regulation* is defined as

$$\epsilon = \frac{(\text{no-load voltage}) - (\text{full-load voltage})}{(\text{no-load voltage})} \qquad (3.47)$$

assuming a constant applied primary voltage.

The *efficiency* of the transformer is defined as

$$\eta = \frac{\text{output power}}{\text{input power}} \qquad (3.48)$$

$$= \left\{ 1 - \frac{\text{losses}}{\text{output} + \text{losses}} \right\} \qquad (3.49)$$

Power transformers have very high efficiencies – even a 1 kVA transformer will
usually have an efficiency greater than 90 per cent – and the efficiency improves
with increasing size. As with DC machines (section 2.3), the efficiency is calculated from eqn (3.49) by determining the losses, and not from eqn (3.48) by
measuring the input and output power; the power measurements cannot be
made with sufficient accuracy.

Auto-transformers

It is not essential for a transformer to have a separate secondary winding; the alternating core flux will induce an EMF in each turn of the primary winding, and the output can be taken from a portion of the same winding. This single-winding transformer is termed an *auto-transformer* [2]. Because part of the winding is effectively common to the primary and the secondary, there can be a substantial saving in weight and cost if the ratio of input to output voltage is less than about 3:1. Auto-transformers can be used only when electrical isolation is not required between the input and the output. An elegant application of the auto-transformer principle is the variable transformer, which has a single-layer coil wound on a toroidal core. The output is taken from a carbon brush which makes contact with the surface of the coil; the brush can be moved from one end of the coil to the other, thus varying the output voltage.

Instrument transformers

An important application of transformers is to extend the voltage or current ranges of AC measuring instruments for making measurements on high-power circuits. Specially designed transformers known as instrument transformers are used for this purpose [3].

Voltage transformers

A voltage transformer has a high-voltage primary winding connected in parallel with the circuit. It has a low secondary voltage, typically 110 V, which can be safely used by instruments such as voltmeters or wattmeters. The relationship between the primary and secondary voltages is given by eqn (3.40), which can be expressed as follows:

$$V_2 = nV_1 - nI_1(R_1 + jx_1) - I_2(R_2 + jx_2)$$

$$= nV_1 - n(I_0 + nI_2)(R_1 + jx_1) - I_2(R_2 + jx_2) \tag{3.50}$$

From this equation it will be seen that the ideal transformer relationship is modified by two impedance drop terms; it is necessary to make these as small as possible, so that the voltage applied to the instrument approximates to a constant n times the circuit voltage. This condition depends on two factors: the design of the transformer, and its method of use. Voltage transformers are characterised by small values for the series impedance terms – particularly the leakage reactances – and large values for the magnetising reactance and core-loss resistance to make the no-load current I_0 small. These conditions demand a high-quality magnetic core, with a low reluctance and low loss. A voltage transformer should always have a high secondary load impedance to minimise the secondary current

I_2; the operation then approximates to the condition of an open-circuited secondary.

Current transformers

A current transformer has a high-current primary winding which is connected in series with the circuit. The secondary carries a low current, typically 5 A, suitable for instruments such as ammeters or wattmeters. The relationship between the primary and secondary currents is given by eqn (3.39), which can be rearranged as follows:

$$I_2 = I_1/n - I_0/n \qquad (3.51)$$

If the no-load current I_0 is small, then the secondary current approximates to a constant $1/n$ times the circuit current. As with the voltage transformer, there is an unwanted term which must be minimised by the design of the transformer and by the method of use. The no-load current I_0 is given by

$$I_0 = (1/R_0 + 1/jX_m)\{(R_2 + jx_2)I_2 + V_2\}/n \qquad (3.52)$$

where V_2 is the secondary terminal voltage. Unlike the voltage transformer, the performance of the current transformer is not affected by the primary series impedance. The design of the primary winding is therefore not critical; it can take the form of a single conductor inserted through the centre hole of a ring core. As with a voltage transformer, the secondary series impedance must be small, and the shunt terms – R_c and X_m – must be large. This again implies a high-quality magnetic core, which is usually made in the form of a ring wound from a continuous strip of low-loss magnetic material.

The secondary operating conditions for a current transformer are the opposite of those for a voltage transformer; the impedance must be as low as possible, to minimise the secondary voltage V_2. The operation thus approximates to a short-circuit condition. Note that it is perfectly safe to short-circuit the secondary terminals; the current is limited by the external circuit. Conversely, it is dangerous to open-circuit the secondary, for the following reason. With a low impedance connected to the secondary, the magnetising current I_m is small; the primary MMF N_1I_1 is almost balanced by the secondary MMF $-N_2I_2$, leaving the small MMF N_1I_m required to magnetise the core. When the secondary is open-circuited, $I_2 = 0$; but the primary current I_1 continues to flow, so there is now a large MMF N_1I_1 which will drive the core heavily into saturation on each half-cycle of the AC supply. The core flux waveform will be nearly square, and the rapid change from one direction to the other will induce a high voltage in the secondary winding. In a high-quality transformer the induced voltage may be several kilovolts.

Problems

3.1. In a balanced three-phase four-wire system, show that no current will flow in the neutral conductor. Hence show that any balanced three-phase system (three-wire or four-wire) may be resolved into three separate single-phase systems with the voltages, currents and element values in the phases equal to the equivalent star values for the original system.

3.2. A three-phase load consists of three equal impedances of magnitude Z and phase angle ϕ. If the load is star connected, show that the instantaneous flow of power into the load is constant, with a value given by

$$P = \sqrt{3}VI \cos \phi$$

where V is the RMS line voltage, I is the RMS line current and $\cos \phi$ is the load power factor. Show that this expression also holds when the load is delta connected, and find the ratio of the line currents in the two cases.

3.3. The Scott connection of two transformers, shown in figure 3.21, is used for

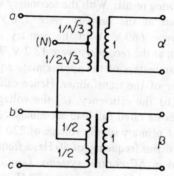

Figure 3.21 Scott transformer connection

obtaining a two-phase supply α, β from a three-phase supply a, b, c with an optional neutral connection N. The transformers (which may be assumed to be ideal) have tapped primary windings, with the turns ratios indicated in the diagram. Construct a voltage phasor diagram for the system, and verify that the system will transform voltages from three to two phases and vice versa.

3.4. The ideal gyrator is a circuit element invented by Tellegen to complete the set of linear passive elements (resistor, capacitor, inductor, transformer, gyrator). The circuit symbol for a gyrator is shown in figure 3.22, and the defining equations are

$$v_1 = ki_2$$

$$v_2 = ki_1$$

Compare the properties of the gyrator with those of an ideal transformer. If a capacitance C is connected to the output of the gyrator, what does the voltage–current relation at the input represent?

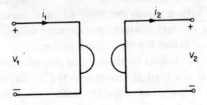

Figure 3.22 Ideal gyrator

3.5. A power transformer has the following nominal rating: primary 220 V, 50 Hz; secondary 660 V, 7.7 A, 5.1 kVA. Open-circuit and short-circuit tests gave the following results. With the secondary winding on open circuit, measurements taken at the *primary* were 220 V, 1.18 A, 65.5 W; the secondary voltage was 669 V. With the primary winding short circuited, measurements taken at the *secondary* were 13.2 V, 7.70 A, 69.5 W.

Calculate the parameters of the approximate equivalent circuit referred to the primary side of the transformer. Hence calculate (a) the secondary terminal voltage, (b) the efficiency, (c) the voltage regulation, when the transformer supplies its rated full-load secondary current of 7.7 A at unity power factor, with a primary supply voltage of 220 V.

3.6. In addition to the mains frequency of 50 Hz, a frequency of 400 Hz is commonly encountered in AC control systems. Consider two transformers of similar rating, one designed for operation at 50 Hz and the other for 400 Hz. When each transformer is operating at its rated voltage and frequency the peak core flux density is 1.3 T and the magnetising current is 5 per cent of the full-load primary current. The transformer cores are made from 4 per cent silicon steel, with a lamination thickness appropriate to the frequency.

By considering the core flux density, the magnetising current and the core loss, explain what will happen if (a) the 400 Hz transformer is operated at 50 Hz; (b) the 50 Hz transformer is operated at 400 Hz. In each case the normal rated voltage is applied to the primary of the transformer. Also explain why the 400 Hz transformer will be smaller and lighter than the 50 Hz transformer.

References

1 H. Waddicor, *Principles of Electric Power Transmission*, 5th ed. (London: Chapman and Hall, 1964).

2 M. G. Say, *Alternating Current Machines*, 5th ed. (London: Pitman, 1983).
3 B. A. Gregory, *Introduction to Electrical Instrumentation and Measurement Systems*, 2nd ed. (London: Macmillan, 1981).

4 Introduction to AC Machines

4.1 Introduction

The commutator in a DC machine performs a complex function which we have not attempted to analyse in detail; the performance equations, on the other hand, are relatively simple. With the AC synchronous and induction machines, the situation is reversed. The absence of a commutator simplifies both the structure and the detailed analysis, but the machine equations are more complex and the basic theory is conceptually more difficult. In this chapter we develop some of the principles which are common to all AC machines by considering the magnetic field set up by currents flowing in the windings. It is convenient to start with the AC generator introduced in the previous chapter.

The simple model of a generator introduced in section 3.2 has a rotor with prominent poles (a 'salient pole' rotor). Many practical machines are in fact made with a rotor structure of this kind, but the general theory is quite complex; an introduction is given in section 5.4. A simpler theory results if the rotor is cylindrical, giving a uniform airgap (figure 4.1); this form of construction is used for mechanical reasons in the high-speed turbine-driven generators of modern power stations. We have seen that a sinusoidal generated voltage is desirable, which implies a sinusoidal variation of the flux density round the rotor when the

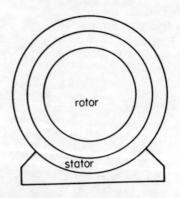

Figure 4.1   AC machine with cylindrical rotor

stator has a simple armature coil as shown in figure 3.1. There are methods of arranging the coils in a practical armature winding to eliminate or reduce some of the harmonics when the flux density variation is not a pure sinusoid, but these are design details which do not concern us here. Whatever may be achieved by subtle design of the armature winding, it is generally necessary to make the flux density variation as nearly sinusoidal as possible. With a salient pole rotor this is accomplished by shaping the poles; with a cylindrical rotor it is achieved by distributing the conductors of the field winding in a particular way.

4.2 Distributed windings and the airgap magnetic field

The coils forming the stator and rotor windings of a practical machine are usually arranged so that the conductors are distributed round the stator and rotor, instead of being concentrated at a number of points as they are in the simple models so far considered. To understand the operation of the machine it is necessary to calculate the magnetic field in the airgap from a knowledge of the current in the winding and the way in which the conductors are distributed; this may be done by an extension of the magnetic circuit concept.

MMF of a distributed winding

Figure 4.2 shows a cross-section through a cylindrical-rotor machine, with conductors distributed round the stator and rotor surfaces. Application of Ampère's

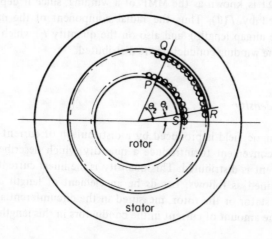

Figure 4.2 Distributed stator and rotor windings

circuital law to the path PQRS gives

$$\Sigma i = \oint H \cdot ds = \int_P^Q H \cdot ds + \int_Q^R H \cdot ds + \int_R^S H \cdot ds + \int_S^P H \cdot ds \tag{4.1}$$

In this equation, Σi is the total current carried by the conductors within the boundary PQRS. If the permeability of the stator and rotor iron is high, the magnetic potential drops along the iron paths QR and SP will be negligible in comparison with the airgap potential drops along PQ and RS. It is reasonable to assume that H is nearly uniform along a radial path in the airgap, so eqn (4.1) becomes

$$\Sigma i = \int_P^Q H \cdot ds + \int_R^S H \cdot ds$$

$$= gH_r(\theta_2) - gH_r(\theta_1) \tag{4.2}$$

where g is the radial length of the airgap, and H_r is the radial component of the magnetising force. Usually, the magnetic field is nearly radial, so that $H_r \approx |H|$; we shall therefore drop the subscript r, with the understanding that the quantity H appearing in the equation is, strictly speaking, the radial component. At some point in the airgap, the value of H will be zero; let the corresponding value of θ be θ_0. At any other value of θ we have

$$\Sigma i = gH(\theta) - gH(\theta_0)$$

$$= gH(\theta) \tag{4.3}$$

where Σi is now the sum of the currents in the conductors between θ_0 and θ. This quantity Σi is known as the MMF of a winding; since it depends on θ, it may be denoted by $F(\theta)$. Thus the radial component of the magnetic field depends on the airgap length g and also on the quantity F, which specifies the way in which the winding conductors are distributed.

Linear current density

Since the magnetic field is produced by a distribution of current-carrying conductors, it is convenient to introduce a quantity which describes the way in which the current is distributed. This quantity is the linear current density K; it is a vector defined as follows. Let ds be an element of length along the iron surface of the stator or the rotor, measured in the circumferential direction. If di represents the amount of current in the conductors in this length ds, then

$$di = K \, ds \tag{4.4}$$

The magnitude of K is thus the current per unit length along the surface, measured perpendicular to the current flow, and the direction of K is the direction of the current. This is similar to the definition of the ordinary current density J (section 1.2), which is also a vector in the direction of current flow but with a magnitude equal to the current per unit area.

Let K_1 and K_2 be the linear current densities on the stator and rotor respectively. The MMF is given by

$$F = \Sigma i = \int di_1 + \int di_2 = \int K_1 \, ds_1 + \int K_2 \, ds_2 \tag{4.5}$$

If r_1 and r_2 are the radii of the stator and rotor surfaces respectively, then

$$F(\theta) = \Sigma i = \int_{\theta_0}^{\theta} K_1 r_1 \, d\theta + \int_{\theta_0}^{\theta} K_2 r_2 \, d\theta \tag{4.6}$$

This expression for the MMF may be substituted in eqn (4.3) to give a direct relationship between the flux density and the current density

$$B(\theta) = \mu_0 H(\theta) = \frac{\mu_0 r_1}{g} \int_{\theta_0}^{\theta} K_1 \, d\theta + \frac{\mu_0 r_2}{g} \int_{\theta_0}^{\theta} K_2 \, d\theta \tag{4.7}$$

Sinusoidally distributed windings

If there is current in only one of the two windings, then eqn (4.7) becomes

$$B(\theta) = \frac{\mu_0 r}{g} \int_{\theta_0}^{\theta} K \, d\theta \tag{4.8}$$

where r and K represent either r_1 and K_1 or r_2 and K_2. If the flux density is to be cosinusoidal, then we may put

$$B(\theta) = B_m \cos \theta \tag{4.9}$$

From eqn (4.8) the required current density is

$$K(\theta) = \frac{g}{\mu_0 r} \frac{dB}{d\theta}$$

$$= -\frac{g B_m}{\mu_0 r} \sin \theta$$

$$= -K_m \sin \theta \tag{4.10}$$

where

$$B_m = \frac{\mu_0 r}{g} K_m \tag{4.11}$$

We thus require a sinusoidal current density in order to produce a cosinusoidal flux density: this is illustrated in figure 4.3, where the size of the small circles

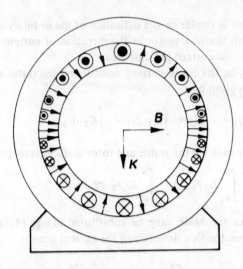

Figure 4.3 Sinusoidal current density and cosinusoidal flux density

represents the magnitude of the current density. Note the right-angle relation-ship between the current-density and flux-density distributions in figure 4.5. This relationship is illustrated by the vectors K and B in figure 4.5, which point in the directions of maximum K and B respectively. These vectors are formally defined in section 4.3.

A sinusoidal current density can, in principle, be produced by distributing the conductors in a non-uniform way. If each conductor carries a current of magnitude i, then the conductor density – the number of conductors per unit length – must vary in the same way as the magnitude of the current density. The small circles in figure 4.3 thus represent the conductor density as well as the current density, and the winding is said to be sinusoidally distributed. Formally we may put

$$K = -K_m \sin \theta = -Zi \sin \theta \tag{4.12}$$

where Z is the maximum number of conductors per unit length, and eqn (4.11) may be written

$$B_m = \frac{\mu_0 r}{g} Zi \tag{4.13}$$

In some special machines such as synchros, which are used as rotary position control devices [1, 2] a close approximation to a true sinusoidal distribution is used. But this is uneconomic for normal AC motors and generators, and for these machines a simpler form of winding is used. It will be shown in section 4.8 that the simple winding can give an acceptably close approximation to the ideal sinusoid.

The concepts of a sinusoidally distributed winding and a sinusoidal magnetic field are of fundamental importance in AC machines. The requirement of a rotor winding of this kind arose from the need to generate sinusoidal voltages in the stator coils. If these coils form part of a distributed stator winding, the magnetic field produced by currents in this winding should have the same form as the rotor field; and this implies that the stator winding should also be sinusoidally distributed. Optimum machine performance is obtained with sinusoidal quantities, and by a happy coincidence this also gives the simplest mathematical treatment. An exactly sinusoidal distribution will therefore be assumed in developing the theory of AC machines.

4.3 Combination of sinusoidally distributed fields

Consider a winding carrying a current i_1, with a conductor distribution such that the current density is

$$K_1 = -K_{1m} \sin(\theta - \alpha)$$

$$= -Z_1 i_1 \sin(\theta - \alpha) \tag{4.14}$$

The magnetic flux density produced by this winding will be

$$B_1 = B_{1m} \cos(\theta - \alpha) \tag{4.15}$$

where

$$B_{1m} = \frac{\mu_0 r_1}{g} Z_1 i_1 \tag{4.16}$$

This sinusoidally distributed field pattern is illustrated in figure 4.4.

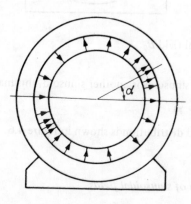

Figure 4.4 Sinusoidal field B_1

Suppose that there is a second sinusoidally distributed winding carrying a current i_2, with a conductor distribution such that the current density is

$$K_2 = -K_{2m} \sin(\theta - \beta)$$

$$= -Z_2 i_2 \sin(\theta - \beta) \tag{4.17}$$

This will give rise to a second magnetic field

$$B_2 = B_{2m} \cos(\theta - \beta) \tag{4.18}$$

where

$$B_{2m} = \frac{\mu_0 r_2}{g} Z_2 i_2 \tag{4.19}$$

This is illustrated in figure 4.5. The total magnetic field B is the sum of the separate fields

$$B = B_1 + B_2$$

$$= B_{1m} \cos(\theta - \alpha) + B_{2m} \cos(\theta - \beta) \tag{4.20}$$

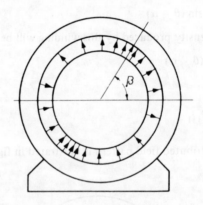

Figure 4.5   Sinusoidal field B_2

Since the sum of two sinusoids is another sinusoid, this may be written as

$$B = B_m \cos(\theta - \gamma) \tag{4.21}$$

and the magnetic field distribution is shown in figure 4.6.

Vector representation of sinusoidal fields

In AC circuit theory the manipulation of sinusoids is simplified by the use of rotating vectors or phasors. A similar device can be used with sinusoidally distri-

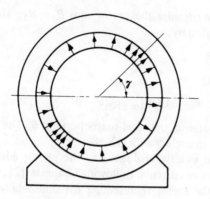

Figure 4.6   Sinusoidal field $B = B_1 + B_2$

buted magnetic fields. We represent a field of maximum value B_m by a radius vector of length B_m, pointing in the direction of the maximum field intensity. Thus in figure 4.7, the field B_1 is represented by a vector $\boldsymbol{B_1}$ of length B_{1m},

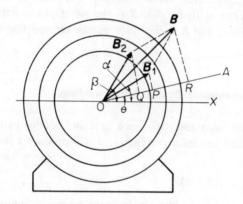

Figure 4.7   Space phasor representation of sinusoidal fields

making an angle α with the reference axis OX; and the field B_2 is represented by a vector $\boldsymbol{B_2}$ of length B_{2m}, making an angle β with the reference axis. Let OA be a line making an angle θ with OX. The projection of $\boldsymbol{B_1}$ on OA is

$$OP = B_{1m} \cos(\alpha - \theta) = B_{1m} \cos(\theta - \alpha) \qquad (4.22)$$

and the projection of $\boldsymbol{B_2}$ on OA is

$$OQ = B_{2m} \cos(\beta - \theta) = B_{2m} \cos(\theta - \beta) \qquad (4.23)$$

Thus the value of the magnetic field at any angle θ in the airgap is equal to the projection of the respective vector on to a line making an angle θ with the reference axis. Now consider the vector sum $B_1 + B_2$. The projection of this vector on to OA is given by

$$OR = OP + PR$$

$$= OP + OQ$$

$$= B_{1m} \cos(\theta - \alpha) + B_{2m} \cos(\theta - \beta) \qquad (4.24)$$

and it therefore represents the total magnetic field B. The length of this vector is B_m, and it makes an angle γ with OX.

This procedure is exactly analogous to the phasor addition of sinusoidally time-varying voltages or currents. Following Chapman [2], we shall use the term 'space phasor' for the vector representing the sinusoidally distributed field, to avoid confusion with the magnetic field vector. Magnetic flux density is a vector quantity possessing magnitude and direction. In developing the theory of electrical machines we are mainly concerned with the radial component of the flux density vector, and in particular with the variation of the scalar magnitude of this component round the airgap. It is the spatial variation of a scalar magnitude which is described by the 'vector' introduced in this section.

Sinusoidally distributed current density may likewise be represented by a space phasor. Thus in figure 4.3, B is the space phasor representing the flux-density distribution, and K is the space phasor representing the current-density distribution.

4.4 Torque from sinusoidally distributed windings

Suppose that the rotor and stator each have sinusoidally distributed windings. If the stator winding carries a current i_1, it will produce a magnetic field of the form

$$B_1 = B_{1m} \cos(\theta - \alpha) \qquad [4.15]$$

and the stator will behave like a permanent magnet with north and south poles. Likewise, if the rotor carries a current i_2 it will produce a magnetic field of the form

$$B_2 = B_{2m} \cos(\theta - \beta) \qquad [4.18]$$

and the rotor will also behave like a permanent magnet. The magnetic axes of the stator and rotor will be displaced by an angle $\delta_{12} = \alpha - \beta$, and there will be a torque on the rotor tending to pull its poles into alignment with the stator poles. This is illustrated in figure 4.8, where the bending of the lines of force is greatly exaggerated. The magnetic field cannot be purely radial, or there would be no torque on the rotor. This follows from the tangential Maxwell stress formula

$$t_s = \frac{B_n B_s}{\mu_0} \qquad [1.43]$$

If the field were purely radial, we would have $B_s = 0$, and therefore $t_s = 0$. It is shown in appendix A that a non-uniform radial magnetic field must be accompanied by a circumferential component; when the stator and rotor axes are displaced, the radial and circumferential components combine to give a field pattern of the form shown in figure 4.8.

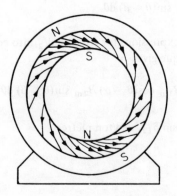

Figure 4.8 Magnetic field for displaced stator and rotor axes

The torque tending to align the magnetic axes of the stator and rotor may be calculated in a number of ways. Energy methods are commonly used [3, 4], but a more direct method is to consider the force acting on the current in each element of the rotor surface; this is merely an extension of the method already used for the DC machine, and it is shown in appendix A that this is equivalent to evaluating the Maxwell stress. Let di_2 be the current in an element of arc $d\theta$; this current will interact with the magnetic field B_1 of the stator to give a force

$$dF = l \times B_1 \, di_2 \qquad (4.25)$$

where l is the axial length of the conductors in the arc $d\theta$. Only the radial component of B_1 will give rise to a circumferential component of dF, and the contribution to the torque is thus

$$dT = -r_2 l B_{1r} \, di_2 \qquad (4.26)$$

where B_{1r} is the radial component of B_1 and r_2 is the radius of the rotor. The negative sign arises from the convention that counter-clockwise torque is positive. Since the value of B_1 calculated from the current distribution is in fact the radial component (see section 4.2), eqn (4.15) may be written in the form

$$B_{1r} = B_{1m} \cos(\theta - \alpha) \qquad (4.27)$$

The current di_2 is given by

$$di_2 = K_2 r_2 \, d\theta$$
$$= -Z_2 i_2 r_2 \sin(\theta - \beta) \, d\theta \qquad (4.28)$$

Since the rotor current i_2 is related to the maximum value B_{2m} of the rotor magnetic field by eqn (4.19), the last equation may be written as

$$di_2 = -\frac{g}{\mu_0} B_{2m} \sin(\theta - \beta) \, d\theta \qquad (4.29)$$

Substitution of these expressions for B_{1r} and di_2 into eqn (4.26) and integrating to obtain the total torque gives

$$T = \int_0^{2\pi} \frac{r_2 lg}{\mu_0} B_{1m} \cos(\theta - \alpha) B_{2m} \sin(\theta - \beta) \, d\theta$$

$$= kB_{1m}B_{2m} \sin \delta_{12} \text{ newton metres} \qquad (4.30)$$

where

$$k = \frac{\pi r_2 lg}{\mu_0} \qquad (4.31)$$

and

$$\delta_{12} = \alpha - \beta$$

Equation (4.30) is an important result, which shows that the alignment torque T varies as the sine of the angular separation δ_{12} between the stator and rotor magnetic axes.

The relation between the component fields B_1 and B_2 and the total field B is given by the space phasor diagram of figure 4.9. Application of the sine rule to this diagram gives

$$\frac{B_{1m}}{\sin \delta_2} = \frac{B_{2m}}{\sin \delta_1} = \frac{B_m}{\sin \delta_{12}} \qquad (4.32)$$

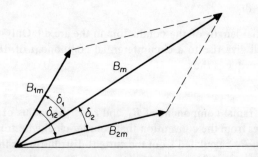

Figure 4.9   Space phasor diagram for displaced stator and rotor axes

The torque equation may therefore be written as

$$T = kB_{1m}B_{2m} \sin \delta_{12} = kB_{1m}B_m \sin \delta_1 = kB_{2m}B_m \sin \delta_2 \qquad (4.33)$$

showing that the torque is proportional to the product of any two of the field components and the sine of the angle between them.

4.5 The rotating magnetic field

The equation

$$B = B_m \cos(\theta - \psi) \qquad (4.34)$$

represents a sinusoidally distributed magnetic field with its axis inclined at an angle ψ. Suppose that this magnetic field is produced by a distributed winding on the stator, and that by some means the angle ψ is made to increase uniformly with time, so that

$$\psi = \psi_0 + \omega t \qquad (4.35)$$

where ω is a constant. For convenience, let $\psi_0 = 0$. The axis, and thus the sinusoidal magnetic field pattern, is rotating in the positive (counter-clockwise) direction with an angular velocity ω. The expression for the magnetic field becomes

$$B = B_m \cos(\theta - \omega t)$$
$$= B_m \cos(\omega t - \theta) \qquad (4.36)$$

and this is the equation of a rotating magnetic field. At any particular instant of time t, eqn (4.36) shows that the field is sinusoidally distributed round the air-gap, with its axis inclined at an angle ωt. The equation also shows that at any particular angle θ the field varies sinusoidally with time, but with a phase lag of θ. This is exactly analogous to a sinusoidal travelling wave of the form $\cos(x - ut)$, encountered in transmission line theory.

It has been seen that a magnetised rotor will experience a torque tending to align its axis with the magnetic axis of the stator. When the stator field rotates, the rotor will rotate in synchronism with it, and this is the basis of the synchronous machine considered in chapter 5. An entirely different kind of machine results if the rotor does not carry fixed magnetic poles, but is made of conducting material or has conductors arranged in suitable closed circuits. If the rotor runs at a lower speed than the rotating field, the rotor will have currents induced in it by the relative motion of the field. These currents will interact with the field to produce a torque on the rotor, and this is the basis of the induction machine studied in chapter 6. We now consider how a rotating stator magnetic field may be produced from fixed windings.

Production of a rotating magnetic field

Suppose that the stator is provided with two sinusoidally distributed windings α and β, which are similar in all respects except that their axes are at $\theta = 0$ and $\theta = \pi/2$ respectively. This arrangement is termed a *two-phase winding*. If the windings carry currents i_α and i_β, the flux density produced by each winding will be

$$\left.\begin{array}{l} B_\alpha = B_{\alpha m} \cos \theta = ci_\alpha \cos \theta \\ B_\beta = B_{\beta m} \cos(\theta - \pi/2) = ci_\beta \cos(\theta - \pi/2) \end{array}\right\} \qquad (4.37)$$

where

$$c = \frac{\mu_0 r_1}{g} Z_1 \qquad (4.38)$$

The total flux density is

$$B = B_\alpha + B_\beta = B_m \cos(\theta - \psi) \qquad (4.39)$$

The amplitude B_m and space phase ψ of the resultant field are given by the space phasor diagram of figure 4.10, from which

$$\left.\begin{array}{l} B_{\alpha m} = B_m \cos \psi \\ B_{\beta m} = B_m \sin \psi \end{array}\right\} \qquad (4.40)$$

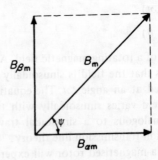

Figure 4.10   Space phasor diagram for a two–phase winding

For a pure rotating field we require B_m = constant and $\psi = \omega t$; from eqns (4.40) and (4.37) we thus have

$$\left.\begin{array}{l} ci_\alpha = B_{\alpha m} = B_m \cos \omega t \\ ci_\beta = B_{\beta m} = B_m \sin \omega t \end{array}\right\} \qquad (4.41)$$

Equation (4.41) will be true if the currents are given by

$$\left.\begin{array}{l} i_\alpha = I_m \cos \omega t \\ i_\beta = I_m \sin \omega t = I_m \cos(\omega t - \pi/2) \end{array}\right\} \tag{4.42}$$

These are the equations of two-phase alternating currents, and it can be concluded that a rotating magnetic field will be produced by two-phase currents flowing in a two-phase winding. This result may also be obtained by direct substitution of eqns (4.42) in eqns (4.37); then

$$\begin{aligned} B &= cI_m (\cos \omega t \cos \theta + \sin \omega t \sin \theta) \\ &= B_m \cos(\omega t - \theta) \end{aligned} \tag{4.43}$$

where

$$B_m = cI_m = \frac{\mu_0 r_1}{g} Z_1 I_m \tag{4.44}$$

Rotating magnetic field with a three-phase winding

A rotating magnetic field may likewise be produced from a symmetrical m-phase supply, provided that the armature also has an m-phase symmetrical winding. Thus for three phases, the fields of the individual armature phases will be

$$\left.\begin{array}{l} B_a = ci_a \cos \theta \\ B_b = ci_b \cos(\theta - 2\pi/3) \\ B_c = ci_c \cos(\theta - 4\pi/3) \end{array}\right\} \tag{4.45}$$

If the windings are supplied from a three-phase source, the currents will be

$$\left.\begin{array}{l} i_a = I_m \cos \omega t \\ i_b = I_m \cos(\omega t - 2\pi/3) \\ i_c = I_m \cos(\omega t - 4\pi/3) \end{array}\right\} \tag{4.46}$$

The total field is $B = B_a + B_b + B_c$, and the airgap flux density is therefore

$$\begin{aligned} B &= cI_m \{\cos \omega t \cos \theta + \cos(\omega t - 2\pi/3) \cos(\theta - 2\pi/3) + \\ &\qquad\qquad + \cos(\omega t - 4\pi/3) \cos(\theta - 4\pi/3)\} \\ &= \tfrac{1}{2} cI_m \{\cos(\omega t - \theta) + \cos(\omega t + \theta) + \cos(\omega t - \theta) + \\ &\qquad + \cos(\omega t + \theta - 4\pi/3) + \cos(\omega t - \theta) + \cos(\omega t + \theta - 8\pi/3)\} \\ &= B_m \cos(\omega t - \theta) \end{aligned} \tag{4.47}$$

where

$$B_m = \frac{3c}{2} I_m = \frac{3\mu_0 r_1}{2g} Z_1 I_m \qquad (4.48)$$

Reversal of the direction of rotation

Interchanging i_b and i_c would give

$$\left.\begin{aligned}
i_{a'} &= i_a = I_m \cos \omega t \\
i_{b'} &= i_c = I_m \cos(\omega t - 4\pi/3) = I_m \cos(\omega t + 2\pi/3) \\
i_{c'} &= i_b = I_m \cos(\omega t - 2\pi/3) = I_m \cos(\omega t + 4\pi/3)
\end{aligned}\right\} \qquad (4.49)$$

With these expressions for current, we obtain

$$B = B_m \cos(\omega t + \theta) \qquad (4.50)$$

which represents a magnetic field rotating in the opposite direction. Thus the direction of rotation of the field may be reversed just by reversing the phase sequence of the supply.

4.6 Voltage induced by a rotating magnetic field

Alternating currents flowing in suitable windings will produce a rotating magnetic field; we now calculate the voltage induced by the rotating field, and find a relationship between the voltage and current for each phase of the winding under balanced operating conditions.

A two-phase machine winding is a natural choice, and this form of winding was used in the early days of AC systems. Since modern power systems use three phases for economic reasons, most industrial machines have three-phase windings. Domestic induction motors are usually single-phase machines, but these are special cases which are considered later in chapter 6. The two-phase machine is now confined almost entirely to AC servo systems [1]; but the principles are virtually the same no matter how many phases are used to produce a uniform rotating field, and only the simpler two-phase model will be analysed in detail. The results may often be generalised to other numbers of phases by inspection, and it may be shown [5] that there is a mathematical transformation which enables the performance of a three-phase machine to be calculated from the analysis of an equivalent two-phase machine. This transformation holds for all conditions of operation: balanced or unbalanced, steady-state or transient; so there is no loss of generality in using a two-phase model.

Voltage induced in a winding

Consider a single-turn coil in the airgap, as shown in figure 4.11, and a rotating magnetic field given by

$$B = B_m \cos(\omega t - \theta) \qquad [4.43]$$

The flux linking this coil is given by

$$\Phi = \int_{-\pi/2}^{\pi/2} Blr \, d\theta \qquad (4.51)$$

where r is the radial distance of a coil side from the axis, and l is the length of each coil side. Evaluating the integral in eqn (4.51) gives

$$\Phi = \int_{-\pi/2}^{\pi/2} B_m lr \cos(\omega t - \theta) \, d\theta$$

$$= 2rlB_m \sin(\omega t + \pi/2) \qquad (4.52)$$

and the induced EMF in the coil is thus

$$e = \frac{d\Phi}{dt} = 2rl\omega B_m \cos(\omega t + \pi/2) \qquad (4.53)$$

This result could also be obtained from the flux cutting rule (eqn 1.5); the velocity of the field relative to the conductor is $u = \omega r$, and the magnitude of the EMF induced in each conductor is

$$e_c = Blu = rl\omega B_m \cos(\omega t + \pi/2) \qquad (4.54)$$

Equation (4.54) is an important step in developing the theory of induction machines (section 6.3), but the use of the flux cutting rule may seem dubious

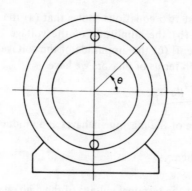

Figure 4.11 Single-turn stator coil

in view of the warning given in section 1.3; the velocity u is certainly not the velocity relative to any material part. The derivation of eqn (4.53), however, is not open to dispute; this shows that the EMF in each conductor is given by eqn (4.54), and it provides the formal justification for using the flux cutting rule with rotating or travelling fields.

If the single-turn coil is replaced by a sinusoidally distributed winding, the induced EMF may be found by integration; for the α-phase winding the result is

$$e_\alpha = \pi r^2 \, lZ\omega B_m \cos(\omega t + \pi/2) \tag{4.55}$$

Relationship between phase voltage and current

Equation (4.55) gives the EMF induced in the α phase by the rotating magnetic field. When the field is itself produced by currents flowing in the two phases of the winding, there is an important relationship between the phase voltage and current. If the winding resistance and leakage reactance may be neglected, the terminal voltage v_α is equal to the induced EMF e_α. The maximum flux density is related to the maximum current in the winding by the equation

$$B_m = \frac{\mu_0 r}{g} \, ZI_m \tag{4.44}$$

and the terminal voltage is therefore given by

$$v_\alpha = \frac{\pi r^3 \, lZ^2 \mu_0}{g} \, \omega I_m \cos(\omega t + \pi/2) \tag{4.56}$$

The current flowing in this phase is

$$i_\alpha = I_m \cos \omega t \tag{4.42}$$

Comparison of the last two equations shows that (a) the voltage leads the current by $\pi/2$ radians; (b) the amplitude of the voltage is proportional to the amplitude of the current; (c) the amplitude of the voltage is proportional to the angular frequency ω. In terms of phasors we have

$$V_\alpha = j\omega \left[\frac{\pi r^3 \, lZ^2 \mu_0}{g} \right] I_\alpha \tag{4.57}$$

showing that this phase of the machine behaves as an inductance of value

$$L = \frac{\pi r^3 \, lZ^2 \mu_0}{g} \quad \text{henrys} \tag{4.58}$$

It is readily shown that the terminal voltage of the β phase is given by

$$v_\beta = \frac{\pi r^3 \, lZ^2 \mu_0}{g} \, \omega I_m \sin(\omega t + \pi/2) \tag{4.59}$$

while the current is

$$I_\beta = I_m \sin \omega t \qquad (4.60)$$

Thus the β phase also behaves as an inductance of value L; the voltage and current have the same magnitudes as those in the α phase, but lag by an angle of $\pi/2$ radians. Similar results hold for a symmetrical m-phase machine; the currents and voltages have the same magnitudes in each phase, but there is a phase shift of $2\pi/m$ between adjacent phases.

Relationship between space and time phasors

Suppose that a machine has windings on the stator which produce a rotating field of the form

$$B_1 = B_{1m} \cos(\theta - \omega t - \alpha) \qquad (4.61)$$

and windings on the rotor which produce a rotating field of the form

$$B_2 = B_{2m} \cos(\theta - \omega t - \beta) \qquad (4.62)$$

These fields will combine to give a total field

$$B = B_m \cos(\theta - \omega t - \gamma) \qquad (4.63)$$

and at any instant of time the magnetic field components may be represented by the space phasors B_1, B_2 and B. Figure 4.12 shows the space phasor diagram for

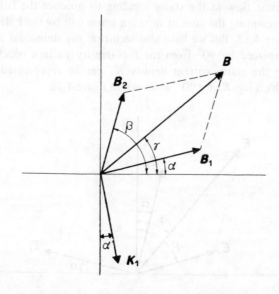

Figure 4.12   Space phasor diagram for stator and rotor fields

the instant $t = 0$, and the phasors may be imagined to rotate with angular velocity ω in the counter-clockwise direction. Each field component acting alone would induce EMFs in the phases of the windings. Consider the EMF e_1 induced in the α phase of the stator winding by the field component B_1. The previous analysis may be used if we let

$$\omega t' = \omega t + \alpha \tag{4.64}$$

Equation (4.61) then becomes

$$B_1 = B_{1m} \cos(\omega t' - \theta) \tag{4.65}$$

and eqn (4.55) gives the induced EMF

$$e_1 = CB_{1m} \cos(\omega t' + \pi/2) = CB_{1m} \cos(\omega t + \alpha + \pi/2) \tag{4.66}$$

where

$$C = \pi r^2 lZ\omega \tag{4.67}$$

Similarly the EMF e_2 induced by the field component B_2 will be

$$e_2 = CB_{2m} \cos(\omega t + \beta + \pi/2) \tag{4.68}$$

and the total EMF e induced by the total field B will be

$$e = CB_m \cos(\omega t + \gamma + \pi/2) \tag{4.69}$$

These EMFs may be represented by the time phasors E_1, E_2 and E shown in figure 4.13, which is drawn for the instant $t = 0$.

Currents must flow in the stator winding to produce the field B_1, and the phasor I_1 representing the current in the α phase will lag the EMF E_1 by $90°$ as shown in figure 4.13. But we have also seen that the sinusoidal current-density pattern is displaced by $90°$ from the flux-density pattern which it produces. Consequently the stator current density K_1 can be represented by the space phasor K_1, which lags B_1 by $90°$, as shown in figure 4.12.

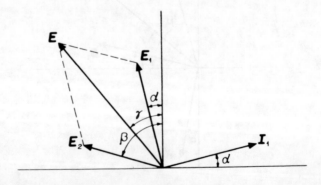

Figure 4.13 Time phasor diagram for one stator phase

There is an exact parallel between the space phasor diagram of figure 4.12 and the time phasor diagram of figure 4.13. The lengths of the time phasors are proportional to the lengths of the corresponding space phasors, and the angles between the phasors are the same in the two diagrams. The relationship between the field components represented by figure 4.12 and the phase voltage and current represented by figure 4.13 is crucial to the theory of AC machines; it leads directly to the equivalent circuit of the synchronous machine in chapter 5, and in a more subtle way to the equivalent circuit of the induction machine in chapter 6. The shift of 90° between the two diagrams will be suppressed in chapters 5 and 6, and time phasors will be drawn parallel to the corresponding space phasors.

4.7 Multi-pole fields

The machine windings so far considered produce two effective magnetic poles, and the field makes one revolution during one cycle of the AC supply. The length of arc between one pole and the next is known as a *pole pitch*, and we may therefore say that the field moves through two pole pitches during one cycle of the supply.

Suppose that we construct a machine having a four-pole rotor and a stator winding that produces a four-pole field (figure 4.14). During one cycle of the supply the field will move through two pole pitches as before, but this represents only half a revolution. The speed of the rotating field is thus $\omega/2$ for a four-pole

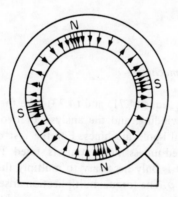

Figure 4.14 Four–pole field

machine, and for a machine with $2p$ poles the speed will be ω/p. The magnetic field will still be sinusoidally distributed, and it will go through a complete cycle in two pole pitches regardless of the number of poles on the machine. It is convenient, therefore, to work in terms of an electrical angle θ_e which increases by

2π for each complete cycle of the field. If the actual angular position or 'mechanical angle' is θ, then the electrical angle is given by

$$\theta_e = p\theta \tag{4.70}$$

This procedure may be justified formally as follows. The field components of a $2p$-pole two-phase winding will be given by

$$\left.\begin{array}{l} B_\alpha = ci_\alpha \cos p\theta \\ B_\beta = ci_\beta \cos(p\theta - \pi/2) \end{array}\right\} \tag{4.71}$$

If a two-phase supply is connected to the winding, the currents will be

$$\left.\begin{array}{l} i_\alpha = I_m \cos \omega t \\ i_\beta = I_m \cos(\omega t - \pi/2) \end{array}\right\} \tag{4.72}$$

The total field is $B = B_\alpha + B_\beta$; from eqns (4.71) and (4.72) this is

$$\begin{aligned} B &= cI_m \cos(\omega t - p\theta) \\ &= cI_m \cos p\left(\frac{\omega}{p}t - \theta\right) \end{aligned} \tag{4.73}$$

When the supply angular frequency is ω, eqn (4.73) shows that a $2p$-pole field will rotate with angular velocity ω/p. This quantity is termed the *synchronous angular velocity*, denoted by ω_s and measured in radians per second.

Analysis of multi-pole machines

If $p\theta$ is replaced by θ_e, eqns (4.71) and (4.73) take the same form as the equations for a two-pole winding, and the analysis of two-pole machines may be applied directly to multi-pole machines. For the rest of this book a two-pole machine will be assumed unless the contrary is stated. To extend the analysis to multi-pole machines, it is only necessary to multiply the synchronous speed by $1/p$ and the torque by p. The torque multiplication arises from the derivation of the torque equation, in which an integral is taken round the whole circumference of the rotor; since this comprises $2p$ pole pitches, or p complete cycles of the field, the torque equation becomes

$$T = pkB_{1m}B_{2m} \sin \delta_{12} \tag{4.74}$$

where δ_{12} is the electrical angle between the axes of the stator and rotor fields. The work done per second by the rotating field is $\omega_s T$, and this is independent of the number of poles.

4.8 Introduction to practical windings

For most of this chapter ideal sinusoidally distributed windings have been postulated, in order to simplify the mathematical treatment. One consequence of a sinusoidal distribution is that the rotating field has a constant amplitude B_m and a constant angular velocity ω_s. These are desirable properties, which ensure that the torque developed by the machine will be a steady quantity. Practical windings are designed to approximate to this ideal, and in this section we show what can be achieved with a fairly simple arrangement of conductors in the form of coils.

Consider a two-phase winding. Figure 4.15 shows a distribution of conductors which gives a stepped approximation to the ideal sinusoid for the α phase, and figure 4.16 shows the corresponding field distribution. Conductors carrying i_α inwards are designated α, and those carrying i_α outwards are designated $\bar{\alpha}$. Similar diagrams for the β phase are shown in figures 4.17 and 4.18. These two conductor arrangements can be combined, as shown in figure 4.19, to form a layer of conductors of uniform thickness. In practice the conductors in a machine are placed in slots, as illustrated in figure 4.20. A conductor carrying current inwards in one slot may be joined with another conductor carrying the same current outwards in another slot to form a coil, as shown in figure 4.21. Since one coil side is at the top of a slot and the other side at the bottom of a slot, the process may be continued in this way all round the periphery; all conductors are joined in pairs to form coils, and all coils have the same shape. Figure 4.22 shows coils of this kind fitted into the stator core of a machine. After winding, the coils are interconnected so that all the conductors of one phase are in series (or possibly in series/parallel groups when the machine has more than two poles). It may be observed that this method of constructing an AC stator winding is very similar to the construction of a DC armature winding mentioned in section 2.1.

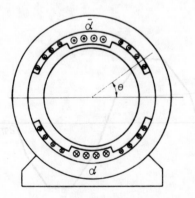

Figure 4.15   Conductor distribution for the α phase

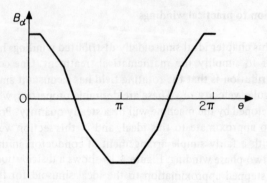

Figure 4.16   Flux density distribution for the a phase

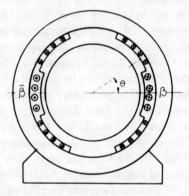

Figure 4.17   Conductor distribution for the β phase

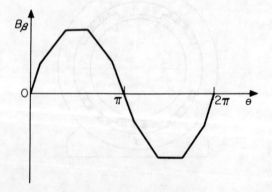

Figure 4.18   Flux density distribution for the β phase

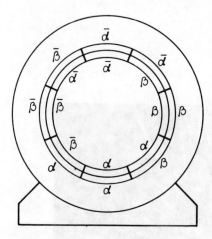

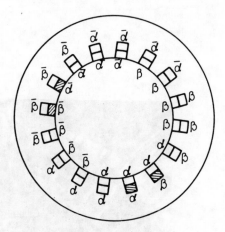

Figure 4.19 Combined two-phase conductor distribution

Figure 4.20 Arrangement of a two-phase winding in slots

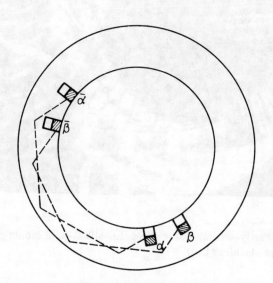

Figure 4.21 Grouping of conductors into coils

Figure 4.22 Partly-wound stator for a 2.6 MW 2-pole induction motor (GEC Alsthom Large Machines Ltd)

The principle of this two-phase winding can be adapted to three phases, where it gives an even better approximation to the ideal. To see why this is so, consider first a winding consisting of a single concentrated coil as in figure 4.11. If the coil is of negligible width, then eqn (4.3) shows that the resulting field distribution will be a square wave because Σi remains constant for nearly $180°$ and then changes sign as θ passes the position of the next coil side. We may therefore express B in terms of the Fourier series for a square wave of amplitide B_m

$$B = \frac{4B_m}{\pi} \left(\cos \theta - \frac{1}{3} \cos 3\theta + \frac{1}{5} \cos 5\theta - \ldots\right) \tag{4.75}$$

This is the worst possible winding, which introduces a series of unwanted space harmonics in addition to the fundamental $\cos \theta$ term. One advantage of a three-phase winding is that harmonics which are multiples of 3 – the triplen harmonics – usually have little effect. In a three-wire star-connected machine, the triplen harmonics cancel completely, regardless of whether the currents are balanced or not. If the winding is spread over several slots, some of the other harmonics are also attenuated, giving a much improved waveform.

In the two-phase winding discussed above, a non-uniform conductor distribution is achieved by using coils which span less than one pole pitch. Figure 4.20 shows that the span is $3/4$ of a pole pitch. For a similar 3-phase winding the span is $5/6$ of a pole pitch, and this has the effect of severely attenuating the 5th and 7th space harmonics. For a winding in 24 slots – the three-phase equivalent of figure 4.20 – the Fourier series is as follows, with the triplen harmonics omitted

$$B = \frac{4B_m}{\pi} (0.933 \cos \theta + 0.013 \cos 5\theta + 0.010 \cos 7\theta +$$

$$+ 0.085 \cos 11\theta + 0.072 \cos 13\theta + \ldots) \tag{4.76}$$

The space harmonics are now insignificant apart from the 11th and 13th, and these could be reduced by using more slots. This is only one of many possible winding arrangements, but the intricacies of practical windings do not concern us here; they are treated in standard texts such as Say [2]. It is sufficient to know that windings can be made to produce an acceptable approximation to the ideal sinusoidal field, and for the purposes of analysis we assume that the field is exactly sinusoidal.

Problems

4.1. In the definition of the MMF of a distributed winding (section 4.1), the summation of currents is taken from a starting point θ_0 for which $H = 0$. If θ_0 cannot be found by inspection, some arbitrary angle, say $\theta = 0$, must be used as the starting point. Then

$$F(\theta) = F'(\theta) + F(0)$$

where $F'(\theta)$ is the sum of the currents in the conductors between 0 and θ, and $F(0)$ is the MMF at the point $\theta = 0$.

Use the fact that the net flux out of a closed surface is always zero to prove that when the airgap length g is a constant the MMF $F(\theta)$ must satisfy the condition

$$\int_0^{2\pi} F(\theta)\, \mathrm{d}\theta = 0$$

Hence show how the value of $F(0)$ may be deduced from a graph of $F'(\theta)$ against θ.

4.2. Extend the analysis of a three-phase winding given in section 4.4 to m phases. Show that the winding will produce a magnetic field rotating with an angular velocity equal to the angular frequency of the supply, and that the amplitude will be constant and equal to $m/2$ times the maximum field produced by any one phase acting alone. Note that the analysis involves the summation of terms of the form $\cos(\omega t + \theta + 4\pi r/m)$ where r is an integer. This is most easily accomplished if the terms are represented by phasors.

4.3. Verify the expression given in eqn (4.55) for the EMF induced in the α-phase winding by considering an elementary coil formed by the conductors in two elementary arcs of angle $\mathrm{d}\theta$, one located at $+\theta$ and the other at $-\theta$. If the conductor density is $Z \sin \theta$, calculate the flux linkage of this elementary coil, and by integrating from $\theta = 0$ to $\theta = \pi$ evaluate the total flux linkage of the winding.

4.4. The relationship between the current density and the airgap flux density is given by eqn (4.8) where g is the radial length of the airgap.

Consider a machine with a circular stator, and a stator winding which produces a rotating current wave given by

$$K = K_\mathrm{m} \cos(\theta - \omega t - \alpha)$$

The machine has an iron rotor with no windings; it is not circular, but is shaped so that the airgap length is given by

$$1/g = A_0 + A_1 \cos 2\phi$$

where ϕ is the angular displacement from a reference axis on the rotor. If the rotor revolves with an angular velocity ω_r, the position of a point on the rotor with respect to the stator is $\theta = \phi + \omega_r t$, and $1/g$ becomes

$$1/g = A_0 + A_1 \cos 2(\theta - \omega_r t)$$

Find the total torque exerted on the stator winding; this will be equal and opposite to the torque exerted on the rotor. Show that the torque will be constant if $\omega_r = \omega$, and compare this machine with the one considered in problem 1.6.

References

1 P. L. Taylor, *Servomechanisms*, 2nd ed. (London: Longman, 1964).
2 M. G. Say, *Alternating Current Machines*, 5th ed. (London: Pitman, 1983).
3 C. R. Chapman, *Electromechanical Energy Conversion* (New York: Blaisdell Publishing Co., 1965).
4 A. E. Fitzgerald, C. Kingsley, Jr. and S. D. Umans, *Electric Machinery*, 4th ed. (New York: McGraw-Hill, 1983).
5 C. V. Jones, *The Unified Theory of Electrical Machines* (London: Butterworths, 1967).

5 *Synchronous Machines*

5.1 Introduction

In its usual form, the synchronous machine consists of a stator with a polyphase winding which produces a rotating magnetic field, and a magnetised rotor having the same number of poles as the stator field. The rotor may incorporate permanent magnets, or it may be magnetised by direct current flowing in a field winding on the rotor. As its name implies, the distinctive feature of the synchronous machine is that the rotor revolves in synchronism with the rotating magnetic field of the stator, and its speed is therefore related to the frequency of the AC supply to the stator.

Synchronous machines can operate as generators or motors; nearly all the large generators in power supply systems are of this kind, and large synchronous motors are widely used as high-efficiency constant-speed industrial drives. Machines of this kind invariably have wound rotors, which permit control of the machine characteristics by varying the rotor excitation. In small machines the DC supply to the rotor is usually taken through brushes and sliprings, but in large machines a brushless excitation system is normally employed as follows. The DC supply to the rotor excitation winding is obtained from a shaft-mounted rectifier supplied by a small AC generator known as an *exciter*; the AC winding of the exciter is mounted on the same shaft as the main machine rotor, and the field winding of the exciter is stationary. Figure 5.1 shows the rotor of a large brushless synchronous generator. With large turbine-driven generators the power loss in the excitation winding is a limiting factor in the design; this loss could be eliminated by using a superconducting winding [1], which offers the prospect of a radically different machine design for ratings above 1000 MW.

The speed of a synchronous motor can be controlled by altering the frequency of the AC supply to the stator. Since the frequency of the AC mains is essentially constant, speed control requires the conversion of electrical power to variable-frequency form, using frequency converters or inverters. This technique can be applied to a wide range of machine sizes; it is the basis of the variable-speed synchronous-motor drive systems described in chapter 8. Small permanent-magnet synchronous motors are particularly suitable for inverter operation, and recent developments [2] claim more power output at a higher efficiency than for an induction motor of the same frame size.

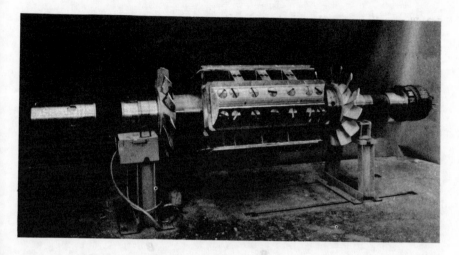

Figure 5.1   Rotor for a 6.2 MVA synchronous generator with brushless excitation (GEC Large Machines Ltd)

Three other types of machine are related to conventional synchronous machines in the sense that they have rotors which move synchronously with a magnetic field generated by windings on the stator. They are: stepper motors, brushless DC motors, and switched reluctance motors. Stepper motors are essentially digital machines, where the rotor is moved in precise steps by switching the stator windings in sequence to a DC supply. This important class of machines is described in chapter 9. Brushless DC machines are described in chapter 10; they may be regarded either as DC machines with the commutator replaced by electronic switches, or as inverter-driven synchronous machines. Switched reluctance drives, described in section 10.4, combine some of the features of synchronous and stepper motors; they have advantages over conventional AC drives in some applications.

This chapter is mainly concerned with the fundamental principles of conventional synchronous machines, and with the use of the excitation winding to control the machine characteristics. An important step in the theory is the development of an equivalent circuit. This concept has already been used with the transformer, to represent the behaviour of magnetically coupled coils by a network of ideal circuit elements (resistors, inductors and an ideal transformer). In a similar way the interaction of currents and magnetic fields in the synchronous machine can be represented by a simple circuit made up of ideal elements, and the characteristics of the machine are readily deduced from the circuit. Thus the equivalent circuit forms a link between the internal electromagnetic processes and the external performance characteristics.

5.2 Phasor diagram and equivalent circuit

We assume that the synchronous machine has a cylindrical rotor, so that it is reasonable to postulate sinusoidally distributed magnetic fields. Figure 5.2 is a space phasor diagram representing the field components at a particular instant of time; the phasors rotate with the synchronous angular velocity ω_s. In this diagram, K_1 represents the current density distribution produced by currents in the stator winding, and B_1 is the corresponding magnetic field; B_2 is the magnetic field produced by currents in the rotor winding; and B is the total or resultant magnetic field. The component fields, acting individually, would induce voltages E_1 and E_2 in one phase of the stator armature winding. The total induced voltage E_t is thus equal to $E_1 + E_2$, as shown in the time phasor diagram of figure 5.3.

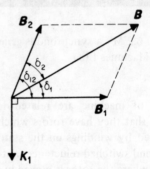

Figure 5.2 Space phasor diagram for an ideal synchronous machine

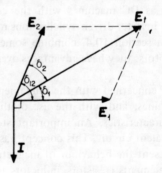

Figure 5.3 Time phasor diagram for an ideal synchronous machine

If the resistance and leakage reactance may be ignored, the total induced voltage E_t will be equal to the terminal voltage V. From eqn (4.57), the component voltage E_1 (due to the stator magnetic field) is related to the stator

current by

$$E_1 = j\omega L_m I = jX_m I \tag{5.1}$$

where L_m is the effective inductance of one stator phase, and X_m is the corresponding reactance. The component E_2 is the contribution of the rotor magnetic field to the total induced voltage; since it depends on the rotor excitation current, it is termed the *excitation voltage*, usually denoted by E. With these changes of nomenclature the phasor diagram of figure 5.3 may be redrawn, taking $V = E_t$ as the reference phasor; the result is shown in figure 5.4, where the angle δ is the same as δ_2 in figure 5.3.

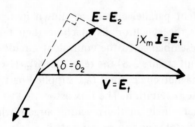

Figure 5.4 Conventional phasor diagram for an ideal synchronous machine

Complete equivalent circuit

Figure 5.4 is the phasor diagram for one stator phase of a synchronous machine; by inspection it is also the phasor diagram for the circuit shown in figure 5.5, which is therefore an *equivalent circuit* of one phase of the machine. The resistance and leakage reactance of the armature winding may be included as elements in series with the reactance X_m, and the stator core loss may be represented by a shunt resistance R_c, to form the complete equivalent circuit shown in figure 5.6.

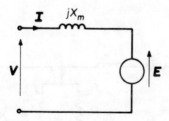

Figure 5.5 Equivalent circuit of an ideal synchronous machine

It is useful to transform the complete equivalent circuit so that the reactance X_m appears as a shunt element; this permits a direct comparison with the equivalent circuit of the induction machine which is derived in chapter 6. The transformation is accomplished by replacing the series combination of E and

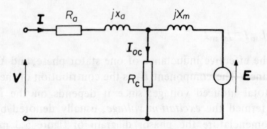

Figure 5.6 Complete equivalent circuit of the synchronous machine

jX_m with an equivalent parallel circuit, as shown in figure 5.7. The complete equivalent circuit for the synchronous machine then takes the form shown in figure 5.8, and the resemblance to the equivalent circuit of the transformer will be noted. In this circuit (figure 5.8) the reactance X_m is a mutual or magnetising reactance, with the magnetising current I_{0m} supplied partly by the stator current and partly by the rotor excitation. The flux associated with this reactance represents the total magnetic field in the machine airgap, which is the resultant of fields produced by the stator and rotor currents.

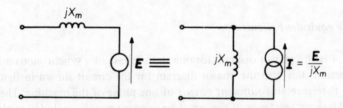

Figure 5.7 Transformation of the excitation branch

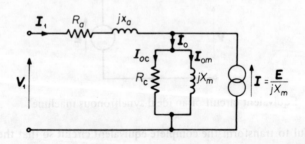

Figure 5.8 Transformed equivalent circuit of the synchronous machine

Approximate equivalent circuit

The armature resistance R_a is often small in comparison with the reactance X_m, and it may be a reasonable approximation to ignore it. If the core loss resistance R_c is also ignored, the two reactances x_a and X_m in figure 5.6 may be combined to form a single reactance X_s, known as the *synchronous reactance*. The equivalent circuit then takes the simple form shown in figure 5.9, which is quite a good

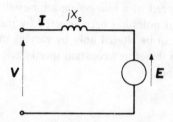

Figure 5.9   Approximate equivalent circuit of the synchronous machine

representation of large machines. With small machines the resistance R_a can be more than 10 per cent of the synchronous reactance X_s, and it should be included in series with X_s if greater accuracy is required. The omission of the core loss resistance R_c has very little effect for most conditions of operation, since the current I_{oc} (figure 5.6) is very small in comparison with the normal value of the total current I.

The phasor equation for the equivalent circuit of figure 5.9 is

$$V = E + jX_s I \tag{5.2}$$

and when the resistance R_a is included this becomes

$$V = E + (R_a + jX_s)I \tag{5.3}$$

The representation of eqn (5.2) by a phasor diagram will be considered in the next section. Equations (5.2) and (5.3) provide an interpretation of the excitation voltage E; when $I = 0$, $V = E$, and E is therefore the open-circuit terminal voltage of the machine.

5.3 Synchronous machine characteristics

The essential features of synchronous machine operation may be derived from the approximate equivalent circuit and the corresponding phasor diagram; before doing so, however, it is useful to make some general deductions from the rotating field concepts.

Synchronous speed

It was shown in section 4.7 that the angular velocity of the rotating magnetic field is given by $\omega_s = \omega/p$, where ω is the angular frequency of the supply and p is the number of pole pairs. If the frequency of the mains supply is f hertz, it follows that the synchronous speed of the machine will be f/p rev/s, or $60f/p$ rev/min. With a mains frequency of 50 Hz the speed of a two-pole machine will be 3000 rev/min, the speed of a four-pole machine will be 1500 rev/min, and so on. Once the number of poles has been selected by the designer, the speed of a synchronous machine can be altered only by varying the supply frequency. The synchronous machine is therefore a constant-speed device when operated directly from the AC mains supply.

Synchronous torque

When the rotor is running at the synchronous speed, its poles will be displaced by a constant angle from the effective poles of the stator. The magnetic lines of force at a particular instant of time are as shown in figure 4.8, and this magnetic field pattern rotates without changing its form. A constant electromagnetic torque is therefore exerted on the rotor, and this will balance the mechanical torque applied to the shaft. The torque equation deduced for stationary fields may therefore be applied to the synchronous machine, giving

$$T = kB_{2m}B_m \sin \delta_2 \qquad\qquad [4.30]$$

Now $B_m \propto V$, $B_{2m} \propto E$ and $\delta_2 = \delta$; the torque equation becomes

$$T \propto VE \sin \delta \qquad\qquad (5.4)$$

and if the terminal voltage V and excitation voltage E are held constant then

$$T \propto \sin \delta$$

Load angle

With the convention that positive values of T and δ correspond to motoring operation, the variation of torque with the angle δ is as shown in figure 5.10. This is an important characteristic of the synchronous machine, and the angle δ is termed the *load angle*; its value varies according to the load applied to the shaft, within the limits of $\pm\pi/2$ radians. Since the speed of the machine is fixed, the torque is entirely determined by the mechanical system connected to the machine shaft. If this is a mechanical load, the torque T will be positive; the synchronous machine will act as a motor, and the positive value of δ implies that the stator poles are ahead of the rotor poles. If a source of mechanical power is coupled to the shaft, T will be negative and the synchronous machine will act as a generator. The angle δ will also be negative, showing that the stator

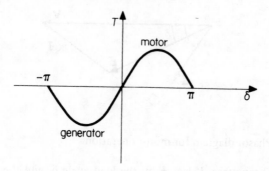

Figure 5.10   Torque/load-angle characteristic for the synchronous machine

poles are now lagging behind the rotor poles. The magnitude of the torque has a maximum value, known as the *pull-out torque*, when $\delta = \pm\pi/2$ radians. If a torque in excess of this value is applied to the machine shaft, the electromagnetic torque cannot balance the shaft torque, and synchronism will be lost.

Damper windings

In the normal working range, the torque/load-angle characteristic is approximately linear; the characteristic resembles that of a spring, where torque increases with displacement. Synchronous machines thus exhibit an electromagnetic 'springiness', and the rotor will tend to oscillate about a mean position if there is any disturbance such as a sudden change in the load. Such oscillations are undesirable, and must be damped; this is normally done electromagnetically, by providing short-circuited windings on the rotor. These windings are known as *damper windings*; they may take the form of conducting paths in solid iron poles or they may be constructed from bars set in slots in laminated poles, like the rotor cage of an induction motor (see chapter 6). During normal synchronous running the flux through a damper winding is constant, and it has no effect; but a change in the load angle will cause the flux to change, and the induced currents will produce a torque which opposes the change.

Synchronous motors and generators

As with the DC machine, there is no essential difference between motoring and generating operation of the synchronous machine. Figure 5.11 shows the phasor diagram when the machine is operating as a motor; the terminal voltage V leads the excitation voltage E by the load angle δ, and the armature current I therefore has a component in phase with V. When the shaft torque is reversed, so that the machine is driven as a generator, the phasor diagram takes the form shown in

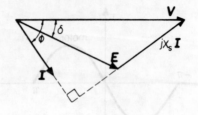

Figure 5.11   Phasor diagram for motor operation

figure 5.12. The voltage V lags E by the load angle δ, and the current I has a component in antiphase with V.

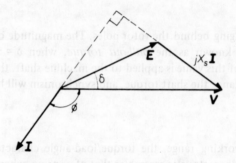

Figure 5.12   Phasor diagram for generator operation

Suppose that the shaft torque gradually changes from a positive (motoring) value to a negative (generating) value, with the magnitudes E and V held constant; the phasor diagram will gradually change from the form shown in figure 5.11 to the one shown in figure 5.12. The locus of E will be an arc of a circle with its centre at O, as shown in figure 5.13, and the locus of I will be another arc with its centre at O$'$. When the torque is zero, the load angle δ will be zero: I will be in quadrature with V, and the electrical power will also be zero.

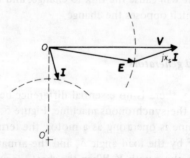

Figure 5.13   Locus diagram for constant excitation

Synchronous motor characteristics

It has already been mentioned that the ability to vary the rotor (or field) excitation is an important feature of the synchronous machine, and we now consider
the effect of such a variation when the machine operates as a motor with a constant load. Similar results hold for the synchronous generator with constant
mechanical input power.

When the torque load on the motor is constant the power output will be
constant, and if losses are neglected there will be a constant input power per
phase given by

$$P = VI \cos \phi \tag{5.5}$$

If the voltage V is constant this equation implies that $I \cos \phi$ is constant, and the
locus of the current phasor I is the line AB in figure 5.14. From this diagram we
have

$$\text{MN} = E \sin \delta = X_s I \sin(\pi/2 - \phi)$$

$$= X_s I \cos \phi \tag{5.6}$$

Thus $E \sin \delta$ is a constant, and the locus of E is the line CD. If $\phi = 0$, the machine
operates at unity power factor and I has a minimum value; let $E = E_0$ for this
condition. When $E < E_0$, ϕ is negative and the machine takes a lagging current,
as shown in figure 5.14; the machine is said to be *under-excited*, and synchronism will be lost when $\delta = \pi/2$. When $E > E_0$, the machine is *over-excited*; ϕ is
positive and the machine takes a leading current (figure 5.15). If the current I is
plotted against the excitation voltage E for different values of the power P, the
result is a set of curves known as V-curves (figure 5.16). A useful characteristic
of the synchronous motor is the leading phase angle of the current when the
machine is over-excited. It can be used to compensate for the lagging current
taken by other loads such as induction motors, so that the total load power
factor is unity. Thus in figure 5.17, if the lagging load current is I_1 and the synchronous motor current I_s is suitably adjusted by controlling the excitation, the
total current I will be in phase with the voltage V. This is known as *power-
factor correction*, and the synchronous machine can be used solely for this
purpose, with no mechanical load connected. Then

$$VI \cos \phi = P \rightarrow 0 \tag{5.7}$$

therefore $I \cos \phi \rightarrow 0$, and the phasor diagram (figure 5.15) shows that $\phi = \pi/2$.
Since the current leads the voltage by approximately $\pi/2$ radians, the machine is
known as a *synchronous capacitor*; it is also known as a *synchronous com-
pensator*.

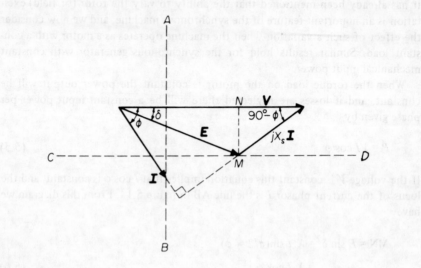

Figure 5.14 Locus diagram for constant power

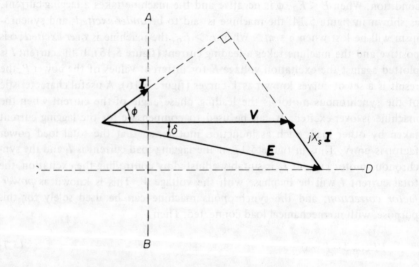

Figure 5.15 Leading power–factor condition

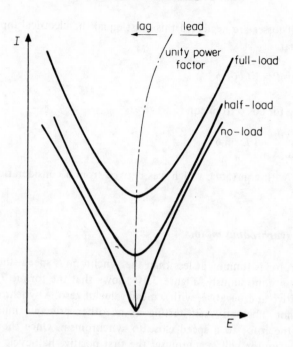

Figure 5.16 Synchronous motor V-curves

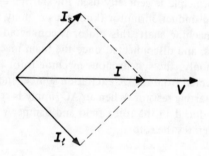

Figure 5.17 Power-factor correction

Torque equation

The torque equation for the synchronous motor may be deduced from the phasor diagram. Let $\omega_s = \omega/p$ be the synchronous angular velocity; the total mechanical output power is $\omega_s T$, and if there are m phases the power per phase is $\omega_s T/m$. If losses are neglected this must equal the electrical input power per phase, so that

$$\frac{\omega_s T}{m} = P = VI \cos\phi \qquad (5.8)$$

Substituting for $\cos\phi$ from eqn (5.6) gives

$$T = \frac{m}{\omega_s X_s} VE \sin\delta \qquad (5.9)$$

This agrees with eqn (5.4), which was derived from a consideration of the magnetic fields.

Starting of synchronous motors

When the rotor is running at less than the synchronous speed, the load angle δ will increase continuously. Figure 5.10 shows that the torque T will be alternately positive and negative, with a mean value of zero. A synchronous motor is therefore not inherently self-starting; some other principle must be used to accelerate the rotor to a speed close to synchronism. Once the speed is high enough, the motor will synchronise; the first positive half-cycle of torque will pull the rotor into step with the rotating field.

Induction motors develop a positive torque at speeds down to zero, and the induction motor principle is generally used for starting synchronous machines. Occasionally a small induction motor (known as a 'pony motor') is coupled to the synchronous machine shaft; this motor is connected to the AC supply for the starting process, and disconnected once the main machine rotor is synchronised. More commonly, the synchronous machine rotor itself is used; the field winding is disconnected from the DC excitation source, and either short-circuited or connected to a starting resistor. When an AC supply is connected to the stator, currents will be induced in the rotor field and damper windings, resulting in a torque which accelerates the rotor.

5.4 Salient-pole synchronous machines

The theory developed in this chapter is only valid for machines with a uniform airgap, that is, those in which the rotor and the stator bore are both cylindrical. When the rotor has salient poles (as shown in figure 5.18) the reactance is no longer constant. Consider first the magnetic field conditions in a non-salient machine, represented by figure 5.2. When there is no load on the machine, $\delta_{12} = 0$, and the magnetic field B_1 due to stator currents acts in the direction of the N–S pole axis of the rotor. If the load is increased until $\delta_{12} = \pi/2$, then the field B_1 is at right angles to the rotor pole axis. In a salient-pole machine, the

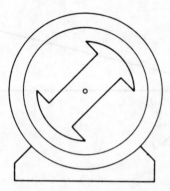

Figure 5.18   Salient-pole synchronous machine

condition $\delta_{12} = 0$ gives a path of easy magnetisation (low reluctance) along the rotor pole axis; this is termed the *direct axis*, and the corresponding reactance at the machine terminals has a high value X_d. The condition $\delta_{12} = \pi/2$ gives a path of difficult magnetisation (high reluctance) along an axis at right angles to the rotor pole axis; this is termed the *quadrature axis*, and the corresponding reactance at the machine terminals has a low value X_q. It is no longer possible to represent the machine by a simple equivalent circuit, but a phasor diagram can be developed as follows.

Let the stator current I be resolved into a component I_d at right angles to E and a component I_q parallel to E, as shown in figure 5.19. The component I_d will produce a magnetic field acting on the direct axis, and the component I_q will produce a magnetic field acting on the quadrature axis. The voltages induced by these field components are represented by the phasors jX_dI_d and jX_qI_q respectively; the terminal voltage V is the phasor sum of these two components together with the voltage E induced by the magnetised rotor. The effect of the armature resistance R_a has been ignored in this diagram; if required, it can be included as a voltage drop R_aI added to E.

The torque equation may be derived from the phasor diagram by expressing the power $VI \cos \phi$ in terms of V, E and δ; if the resistance R_a is neglected, the result is

$$, T = \frac{mp}{\omega}\left[\underbrace{\frac{VE}{X_d}\sin\delta}_{(a)} + \underbrace{\frac{V^2}{2}\left\{\frac{1}{X_q} - \frac{1}{X_d}\right\}\sin 2\delta}_{(b)}\right] \qquad (5.10)$$

Term (a) in this equation represents the normal synchronous torque, which may be identified with eqn (5.9). Term (b) represents a component of torque due to the saliency of the rotor; this component is termed the *reluctance torque*, and it vanishes when the rotor is cylindrical, for X_d is then equal to X_q.

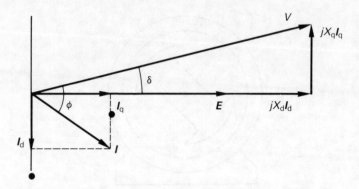

Figure 5.19 Phasor diagram for a salient-pole synchronous machine.

A qualitative explanation of the origin of the reluctance torque is that the salient poles of the rotor will tend to line up with the axes of the stator magnetic field. The torque will be zero when the rotor pole axis is in line with the stator field axis, and zero again when the rotor pole axis is at right angles to the stator field axis. In contrast, the synchronous torque will have a maximum or a minimum value when the two axes are at right angles. The reason for the difference is that the reluctance torque is dependent on the induced magnetisation of the rotor, which varies with the rotor position; whereas the synchronous torque depends on the rotor magnetisation produced by the field winding, and this is independent of the rotor position. Thus in eqn (5.10), the reluctance torque varies as $\sin 2\delta$, while the synchronous torque varies as $\sin \delta$. The torque/load-angle characteristic for a salient-pole machine therefore takes the form shown in figure 5.20.

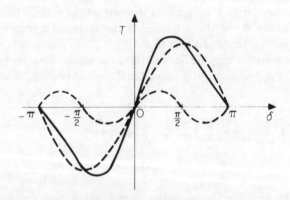

Figure 5.20 Torque/load-angle characteristic for a salient-pole synchronous machine

Reluctance motors

An interesting possibility is to omit the rotor field winding from a salient-pole synchronous motor, so that only the reluctance torque term remains in eqn (5.10). Machines of this kind are known as *reluctance motors* [3], and they normally incorporate on the rotor an induction starting winding of the cage type (see chapter 6). For good performance the rotor must be designed to make the reactance ratio X_d/X_q as large as possible; the simple salient-pole construction is not the best form of the rotor, and commercial motors use other devices such as flux barriers or segmentation to improve the performance [3]. Reluctance motors combine the advantages of the cage induction motor with the speed characteristic of the synchronous machine. They are used in place of induction motors when a constant speed, related to the supply frequency, is required. A typical application is to maintain an absolute speed relationship between a number of widely separated shafts, where mechanical coupling would be difficult.

Linear synchronous motors

The linear induction motor is a well-known type of linear motor, which is derived from the ordinary rotary induction motor (see section 6.7). Synchronous motors can also be made to produce linear motion by changing the geometry from a cylindrical form to a flat form, so that the AC winding generates a travelling magnetic field. The part which carries the AC winding is termed the *primary*; the linear counterpart of the field or excitation system is termed the *secondary*. As with the linear induction motor, a linear synchronous motor can be made with either a short primary or a short secondary. Permanent-magnet short-secondary machines have applications in industry, for example in automated manufacturing systems. Both forms of linear synchronous motor have been considered for advanced passenger transport systems [4, 5]. If the secondary forms part of the track for the vehicle, it is undesirable to have either permanent magnets or an excitation winding on the track. McLean [5] describes several types of linear synchronous motor in which both the DC excitation winding and the AC winding are on the primary, leaving the secondary entirely passive. An alternative is to use a linear form of the reluctance motor [5, 6], which requires no secondary excitation; the primary then takes the same form as the primary of a linear induction motor (see figure 6.24). The linear reluctance motor is the simplest of the linear synchronous motors, but its electrical performance is inferior to that of an excited-secondary motor, so it is unlikely to be used for commercial transport systems.

A recent development of the linear reluctance motor is the short-secondary form for industrial applications such as materials handling [7]. The primary has the form shown in figure 6.24; the secondary comprises several steel segments, mounted on a non-magnetic carrier, which move synchronously with the magnetic field of the primary. This motor can provide linear motion inside a closed vessel; potential applications include the handling of toxic or hazardous materials, or materials which must be kept free from contamination. In this kind of application the active primary is placed on the outside of the vessel, with the simple passive secondary on the inside. The wall of the vessel must be non-magnetic, but it may be metallic. With materials such as stainless steel, eddy-current losses in the wall are usually less than the I^2R loss in the primary winding for speeds of up to 1 m/s [8].

Problems

5.1. A three-phase star-connected synchronous generator has a reactance of 10 Ω per phase, and it operates with a constant line voltage of 520 V. When the generator is delivering its normal rated power, the line current is 40 A and the power factor is unity. Calculate the output power and the magnitude of the excitation voltage per phase under these conditions.

　　With the excitation voltage unchanged, the output power of the generator is increased to its maximum value. Calculate the new values of line current, power factor and output power.

5.2. In the steady state a synchronous motor operates with a load angle δ_0 and it delivers a torque T_0 to the load. A momentary fall in the supply voltage causes the load angle to increase by a small amount, and after the voltage disturbance has passed the load angle is given by

$$\delta = \delta_0 + \epsilon$$

If the electromagnetic torque is then given by

$$T = T_0 + \Delta T$$

show that

$$\Delta T = \frac{T_0}{\tan \delta_0} \epsilon$$

It may be assumed that the machine has a cylindrical rotor; that the steady-state equations are applicable; and that the armature resistance may be neglected.

5.3. If the torque load on the motor in problem 5.2 remains unchanged, show that the rotor equation of motion is

$$\frac{J}{p} \frac{d^2 \epsilon}{dt^2} + \frac{T_0}{\tan \delta_0} \epsilon = 0$$

where J is the moment of inertia of the rotor and p is the number of pole pairs. Hence show that there will be small oscillations superimposed on the steady motion of the rotor, and find the frequency of the oscillations.

5.4. With the machine considered in problem 5.3, show that there will be an alternating voltage induced in the rotor field winding, and explain what effect this might be expected to have on the motion of the rotor.

5.5. Derive eqn (5.10) for the torque of a salient-pole synchronous motor from the phasor diagram in figure 5.19.

References

1 J. R. Bumby, *Superconducting Rotating Electrical Machines* (Oxford University Press, 1983).

2 K. J. Binns and T. M. Wong, 'Analysis and performance of a high-field permanent-magnet synchronous machine', *IEE Proc. B, Electr. Power Appl.*, **131** (1984), pp. 252-8.

3 M. G. Say, *Alternating Current Machines*, 5th ed. (London: Pitman, 1983).

4 B. V. Jayawant, *Electromagnetic Levitation and Suspension Techniques* (London: Edward Arnold, 1981).

5 G. W. McLean, 'Review of recent progress in linear motors', *IEE Proc. B, Electr. Power Appl.*, **135** (1988), pp. 380-416.

6 J. D. Edwards and A. M. El-Antably, 'Segmental-rotor linear reluctance motors with large airgaps', *Proc. IEE*, **125** (1978), pp. 209-14.

7 J. D. Edwards, M. A. Preston and G. Williams, 'Forces in short-secondary linear reluctance motors', *IEEE Trans. on Magnetics*, **MAG-23** (1987), pp. 2929-31.

8 J. D. Edwards and M. A. Preston, 'Forces in screened-secondary linear reluctance motors', *IEE Trans. on Magnetics*, **MAG-24** (1988), pp. 2913-15.

6 Induction Machines

6.1 Introduction

An essential feature of the operation of the synchronous machine is that the rotor runs at the same speed as the rotating magnetic field produced by the stator winding; the magnetic field as 'seen' from a point on the rotor does not vary with time. A very different type of machine results if the rotor is allowed to run more slowly than the rotating field; the rotor will 'see' a rotating field moving past it at the difference of the two speeds, and this field can induce currents in conductors on the rotor. The currents will interact with the rotating field to produce a torque, and this is the basic principle of the induction motor.

In common with other rotating machines, induction machines can operate as motors or generators. For reasons that will be discussed later, induction generators have a very limited use, and nearly all electric power is generated by synchronous machines. Induction motors, on the other hand, are used in far greater numbers than any other type of machine; they range in power rating from a few watts to tens of megawatts. The simplicity of the induction principle is reflected in the robust, reliable and relatively inexpensive construction of the machine itself, and the induction machine is the natural choice in the majority of motor applications.

The stator of an induction motor is similar to that of a synchronous motor, but the rotor structure is different. There are two forms of rotor: the cage rotor and the wound rotor. In a cage rotor, the conductors are in the form of bars (usually of aluminium or a copper alloy) which pass through slots in the laminated iron core of the rotor. The bars are connected to low-resistance rings (known as *end-rings*) at each end of the core, so that any pair of conductors forms a short-circuited turn. Cage rotors are cheap and robust, and in small sizes the bars and end-rings are die cast in a single operation. Figure 6.1 shows the construction of a small cage induction motor, and figure 6.2 shows the cage rotor of a large machine. It is possible to make the rotor in the same way as the stator, with a three-phase winding; an external resistor is connected to each phase of the rotor through sliprings, and the characteristics of the motor can be altered by varying the resistance. Figure 6.3 shows a typical rotor of this kind; it is much more expensive than the cage rotor, and is used only for special applications – see sections 6.4 and 6.5. Motors of this kind are known as *wound-rotor* or *slipring induction motors*. Wound rotors are also used in machines

148

Figure 6.1 Construction of a small cage induction motor (GEC Alsthom Electromotors Ltd)

Figure 6.2 Cage rotor for a 21 MW 4-pole induction motor (GEC Alsthom Large Machines Ltd)

Figure 6.3 Wound rotor for a 1.6 MW 8-pole slipring motor (GEC Alsthom Large Machines Ltd)

known as *synchronous induction motors*; these operate as induction motors for starting, and are then made to run as synchronous motors by passing direct current through the rotor winding.

6.2 Electromagnetic action

The stator (or 'primary') winding of an induction machine is similar to that of a synchronous machine, and when connected to a suitable AC supply it will produce a rotating magnetic field of the form given by eqn (4.36)

$$B_1 = B_{1m} \cos(\omega t - \theta) \tag{6.1}$$

This equation implies that the machine has only two poles, and for simplicity the analysis in this section and in section 6.3 will be given for a two-pole machine. The results are extended at the beginning of section 6.4 to the general case of a $2p$-pole machine.

Suppose that the rotor of the induction machine rotates with an angular velocity ω_r, so that at time t a reference axis on the rotor makes an angle given by

$$\psi = \omega_r t \tag{6.2}$$

with the reference axis of the stator (figure 6.4). Let ϕ be the angular position

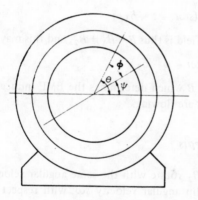

Figure 6.4 Angles and reference axes in the induction motor

of a point on the rotor, measured from the rotor reference axis; then the angle measured from the stator reference axis is

$$\theta = \phi + \psi = \phi + \omega_r t \tag{6.3}$$

Substitution of this expression for θ in eqn (6.1) gives the magnetic field in terms of the angle ϕ

$$B_1 = B_{1m} \cos\{(\omega - \omega_r)t - \phi\} \tag{6.4}$$

This equation implies that the rotor 'sees' a magnetic field rotating past it with an angular velocity of $\omega - \omega_r$, known as the *slip angular velocity*. The quantity

$$s = \frac{\omega - \omega_r}{\omega} \tag{6.5}$$

is termed the *fractional slip*, and we may rewrite eqn (6.4) in the form

$$B_1 = B_{1m} \cos(s\omega t - \phi) \tag{6.6}$$

This rotating field will induce an EMF at the slip angular frequency $s\omega$ in any conductor on the rotor.

Rotor magnetic field

Consider a rotor with a cage winding. An EMF at the slip angular frequency $s\omega$ will be induced in any conductor, and a current at this frequency will flow. The EMF is related to the flux density by eqn (4.54); consequently a pattern of currents will be set up in the rotor conductors which is similar in form to the magnetic field, and this pattern will rotate at the same speed $s\omega$. These rotor currents will in turn set up a rotating magnetic field of the form

$$B_2 = B_{2m} \cos(s\omega t - \phi - \delta_{12}) \qquad (6.7)$$

The total magnetic field is thus $B = B_1 + B_2$, and this may be written as

$$B = B_m \cos(s\omega t - \phi - \delta_1) \qquad (6.8)$$

It is this total field B which determines the EMF induced in a rotor conductor when rotor currents are flowing.

Rotating field concepts

The fields B_1 and B_2 rotate with the same angular velocity; with respect to the rotor, this is the slip angular velocity $s\omega$; with respect to the stator it is the synchronous speed ω. Since there is a constant angle δ_{12} between the axes of the fields, there will be a constant torque on the rotor given by

$$T = kB_{1m}B_{2m} \sin \delta_{12} \qquad [4.30]$$

The mechanism of torque production is thus the same as in the synchronous machine, but the principle of operation is very different. In the synchronous machine, the rotor magnetic field is set up by externally impressed currents, and its axis is fixed relative to the rotor material. The rotor magnetic field of an induction machine, on the other hand, is produced by induced currents in the rotor, and its axis rotates relative to the rotor material. This rotation, or slipping, of the field past the rotor is an essential feature of induction motor operation; if the rotor ran at the synchronous speed it would 'see' a steady field, and there would be no induced currents.

6.3 Equivalent circuit

In order to predict the performance characteristics, it is necessary to construct an equivalent circuit which will represent the machine in terms of lumped circuit parameters and the stator terminal voltage and current. This may be done by considering the relationships between the magnetic field components, the currents flowing in the stator and rotor windings, and the EMFs induced in those windings. The fact that the rotor currents are induced from the stator makes the derivation of the equivalent circuit more difficult than the corresponding derivation for the synchronous machine.

Equivalent circuit of an ideal machine

Consider an induction machine with a cage rotor. The EMF induced in one rotor conductor may be calculated by the flux cutting rule in the same way as in eqn (4.54)

$$e_c = Blu = rls\omega B_m \cos(s\omega t - \phi - \delta_1) \qquad (6.9)$$

If magnetic leakage is neglected, then a current proportional to this EMF will flow in the conductor. Thus a pattern of induced currents will be set up in the rotor with a distribution which matches the sinusoidal distribution of the magnetic field.

Equation (6.9) shows that there will be no induced EMF, and therefore no current, when $s = 0$; the rotor speed ω_r is then equal to the rotating field speed ω. Figure 6.5 shows the stator current density and the airgap flux density under these conditions, while figures 6.6 and 6.7 show the corresponding space and time phasor diagrams. It is assumed for the present that there is negligible stator resistance or leakage reactance, so that the stator terminal voltage V_1 is equal to the EMF induced by the rotating field.

Suppose that the rotor speed ω_r is allowed to fall below the synchronous speed ω, but the stator terminal voltage V_1 is held constant. Current will flow in the rotor, as shown in figure 6.8. Since the stator voltage is constant, the total

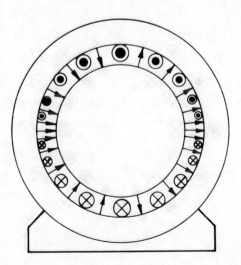

Figure 6.5   Current–density and flux–density distributions for $\omega_r = \omega_s$

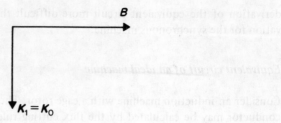

Figure 6.6   Space phasor diagram for $\omega_r = \omega_s$

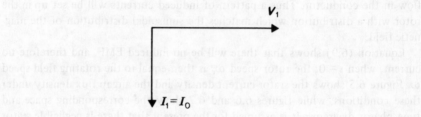

Figure 6.7   Time phasor diagram for $\omega_r = \omega_s$

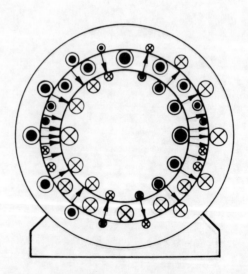

Figure 6.8   Current-density and flux-density distributions for $\omega_r < \omega_s$

flux density B must remain constant; this means that the stator current density K_1 must change in order to counteract the effect of the rotor current density K_2. We may consider K_1 to be made up of two parts, as shown in figures 6.8 and 6.9: a component K_2' which is equal and opposite to the rotor current density K_2, and a component K_0 which sets up the magnetic field. There will be corresponding current components I_2' and I_0 (figure 6.10), which make up the total stator phase current I_1.

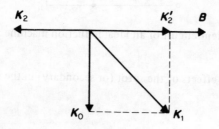

Figure 6.9   Space phasor diagram for $\omega_r < \omega_s$

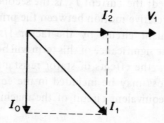

Figure 6.10   Time phasor diagram for $\omega_r < \omega_s$

From eqn (6.9) the induced EMF, and therefore the rotor current, will be proportional to the fractional slip s and to the magnitude of the flux density B_m. It follows that the current I_2' will be proportional to s and to V_1, and we may put

$$I_2' = \frac{sV_1}{R_2'} = \frac{V_1}{R_2'/s} \tag{6.10}$$

The current I_0 is related to the voltage V_1 by eqn (4.57), so that

$$I_0 = \frac{V_1}{jX_m} \tag{6.11}$$

Equations (6.10) and (6.11) are the equations of the circuit shown in figure 6.11, which is the equivalent circuit for an ideal induction machine. The element

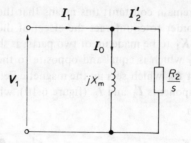

Figure 6.11　Equivalent circuit of an ideal induction machine

R'_2/s represents the effects of the rotor (or secondary) in the stator (or primary) circuit.

Complete equivalent circuit

The similarity of the induction motor to a transformer with a closed secondary circuit should be noted; the current I'_2 is the secondary (rotor) current referred to the primary. The relative motion between the primary and secondary is represented in the equivalent circuit by the factor $1/s$ multiplying the secondary resistance R'_2, and the significance of this term will be explained later. By analogy with the transformer, the effects of stator resistance, stator and rotor leakage reactance and core loss may be included in the equivalent circuit. Figure 6.12 shows the complete equivalent circuit of the machine obtained in this way.

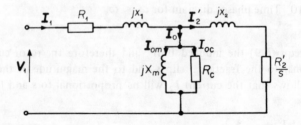

Figure 6.12　Complete equivalent circuit of the induction machine

It is instructive to compare the equivalent circuit of the induction machine with the complete equivalent circuit of the synchronous machine shown in figure 5.8. In the synchronous-machine equivalent circuit, the rotor is represented by an active element − a current generator − which is capable of supplying some or all of the magnetising current I_{0m}. In the induction machine, on the other hand, there is no external rotor excitation; the rotor is represented by a passive element in the equivalent circuit, and all the magnetising current must be drawn from the stator supply. This means that an induction motor necessarily behaves as an inductive load, taking current at a lagging power factor.

Approximate equivalent circuit

The equivalent circuit shown in figure 6.12 is a fairly accurate representation of the machine, and it may be used to predict the characteristics. The analysis is greatly simplified, however, if two approximations are made. First the shunt elements R_c and X_m are transferred to the input terminals. This was shown to be a good approximation with a power transformer (see section 3.4); it is less satisfactory with the induction machine, because the airgap between the stator and rotor reduces the value of X_m and increases x_1, in comparison with a transformer of similar rating. The second approximation is to ignore the stator resistance R_1 in comparison with the term R_2'/s. This is a good approximation when the slip is small, and the equivalent circuit then takes the form shown in figure 6.13; the primary and secondary leakage reactances are combined to give a total leakage reactance $X = x_1 + x_2'$. This simplified circuit demonstrates the essential features of induction motor performance, and the complete equivalent circuit can always be used when a more accurate calculation is required.

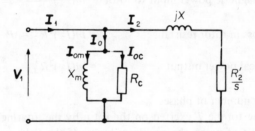

Figure 6.13   Approximate equivalent circuit of the induction machine

6.4 Induction machine characteristics

Multi-pole machines

If the machine stator winding has p pairs of poles, the synchronous speed is $\omega_s = \omega/p$. The fractional slip is now defined as

$$s = \frac{\omega_s - \omega_r}{\omega_s} \tag{6.12}$$

and the slip angular velocity is $\omega_s - \omega_r = s\omega_s$. Since the rotor currents also generate p pairs of poles, the angular frequency of the rotor currents will be p times the slip angular velocity: $ps\omega_s = s\omega$. Thus for a given slip, the rotor frequency is unchanged. The basic electromagnetic action is also unchanged, and the same equivalent circuit holds for a machine with any number of pole pairs.

Rotor power relationships

In the equivalent circuit of figure 6.12, the power loss in R_1 and R_c represents the primary copper loss and the core loss. The power loss in the resistance R'_2/s must therefore represent the average input of power to the rotor, for there can be no dissipation of power in the reactances X_m and x'_2. Thus the input of power per phase to the rotor is $(I'_2)^2 R'_2/s$; but the power dissipated in the actual resistance of the rotor circuit is only $(I'_2)^2 R'_2$. The difference between these quantities is

$$(I'_2)^2 R'_2 \frac{1-s}{s}$$

and this must represent electrical energy converted into mechanical form. If P is the total power absorbed by the rotor, then

electromagnetic power input to rotor $= m(I'_2)^2 \dfrac{R'_2}{s} = P$ (6.13)

power loss in rotor resistance $= m(I'_2)^2 R'_2 = sP$ (6.14)

mechanical power output $= m(I'_2)^2 R'_2 \dfrac{1-s}{s} = (1-s)P$ (6.15)

where m is the number of phases.

Consider the torque T exerted on the rotor by the rotating magnetic field. If there are p pairs of poles, the angular velocity of the field is $\omega_s = \omega/p$, and the rotating field therefore does work at the rate $\omega_s T$. This would obviously be true if the rotating field were produced by physical poles on the stator, driven mechanically at a speed ω_s; the electromagnetic field is the same when a polyphase winding produces the rotating field, so the work done must be the same. Since the rotor runs at a speed $\omega_r = (1-s)\omega_s$, the mechanical power output is $\omega_r T = (1-s)\omega_s T$. The difference between the work done by the field and the mechanical output must be absorbed in rotor losses, so this is $(\omega_s - \omega_r)T = s\omega_s T$. Thus

electromagnetic power input to rotor $= \omega_s T$ (6.16)

power loss in rotor resistance $= (\omega_s - \omega_r)T = s\omega_s T$ (6.17)

mechanical power output $= \omega_r T = (1-s)\omega_s T$ (6.18)

Note that the fraction of the input power lost in rotor resistance is equal to the fractional slip s; since there must always be some slip between the rotor and the rotating magnetic field, this represents an unavoidable power loss. The ratio of mechanical power output to electromagnetic power input is termed the *rotor efficiency*, and its value is $1 - s$.

Torque/speed characteristics

The torque may be calculated for a given value of slip by equating expressions (6.13) and (6.16) for electromagnetic power, and obtaining the value of I'_2 from the equivalent circuit of figure 6.13. For a machine with m phases and p pole pairs, the result is

$$T = \frac{mp}{\omega} \cdot \frac{R'_2}{s} \cdot \frac{V_1^2}{X^2 + (R'_2/s)^2} \tag{6.19}$$

which may be written in the alternative form

$$T = \frac{mp}{\omega} \cdot \frac{V_1^2}{X} \cdot \frac{1}{sX/R'_2 + R'_2/sX} \tag{6.20}$$

Since the slip s is related to the rotor speed ω_r by eqn (6.12), eqn (6.20) gives the torque/speed relationship for the induction machine. Figure 6.14 shows a typical torque/speed or torque/slip characteristic. Note that there can be no induced rotor currents when $s = 0$ and $\omega_r = \omega_s$, so the torque must be zero at this point. There are three distinct regions to the torque/speed characteristic shown in figure 6.14, which will be considered in turn.

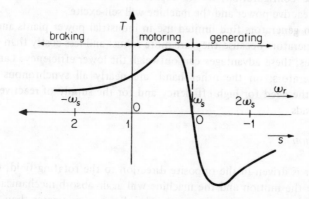

Figure 6.14 Torque/speed characteristic for the induction machine

Motoring region

In this region the rotor speed ω_r is positive but less than the synchronous speed ω_s; the torque is also positive, and the machine converts electrical power into mechanical power. The value of the slip s varies from 1 when the rotor is stationary to 0 when the rotor runs at the synchronous speed. In the complete equivalent circuit (figure 6.12) the resistance R_2'/s is positive and greater than R_2'; thus the total electrical power absorbed by the rotor exceeds the power dissipated in the rotor resistance, and the balance is extracted as mechanical power at the shaft. Since the overall efficiency of the machine cannot exceed the rotor efficiency of $1 - s$, induction motors normally operate with a small value of slip. The full-load slip can be as low as 1 per cent in large machines and seldom exceeds 5 per cent in small machines, so the normal rotor speed is always close to the synchronous speed.

Generating region

When the rotor is driven mechanically so that its speed exceeds the synchronous speed, the torque reverses and the machine absorbs mechanical power. The slip is negative in this region, and the resistance R_2'/s is also negative; the rotor therefore exports electrical power to the stator, and the machine acts as a generator.

The machine requires an external source of reactive power before it will act as a generator, since the magnetising current flowing in X_m cannot be provided by the rotor. In contrast, the synchronous machine provides its own magnetising current by having a field winding on the rotor; an external source is not required. An induction generator is normally connected to an AC supply system which provides the reactive power. It is also possible to operate an induction generator without an external AC supply by connecting capacitors to the stator terminals in a 3-phase configuration; if the capacitors are correctly chosen, they will supply the reactive power and the machine will self-excite.

Induction generators find limited use in industrial power plants and as wind-powered generators because they are more robust and less costly than synchronous machines; these advantages can outweigh the lower efficiency. Large power-system generators, on the other hand, are nearly all synchronous machines because of the need for high efficiency and for the supply of reactive power to inductive loads.

Braking region

If the rotor is driven in the opposite direction to the rotating field, the torque will oppose the motion and the machine will again absorb mechanical power. It will not, however, act as a generator. The slip is now greater than 1, and the resistance R_2'/s is positive and smaller than R_2'; the electrical power input to the rotor is less than the rotor resistance loss, and the balance is supplied by the mechanical power input. The machine therefore acts as a brake, with both the electrical and the mechanical power inputs dissipated in the rotor resistance.

Operation in the braking region can only take place for short periods on account of rotor heating; it is sometimes used as a method of rapidly stopping an induction motor by 'plugging', as follows. Two of the connections to the three-phase stator are interchanged, thus reversing the direction of rotation of the magnetic field and applying a braking torque to the rotor. The stator supply must be disconnected as soon as the rotor comes to rest, otherwise the rotor will continue to accelerate in the new direction of the rotating field. Another method of braking is to pass direct current through the stator winding: see problem 6.3.

Induction motor torque

Several interesting properties of the torque characteristic may be deduced from eqns (6.19) and (6.20). When the slip is such that $sX/R'_2 = 1$, the torque will have a maximum value given by

$$T_m = \frac{mpV_1^2}{2\omega X} \tag{6.21}$$

This is known as the *breakdown torque*, and a load in excess of this value will stop the motor. The normal operating region lies to the right of the peak, and the normal full-load torque is usually less than half the breakdown torque. If s_m denotes the value of slip corresponding to the maximum torque, then

$$\frac{T}{T_m} = \frac{2}{s/s_m + s_m/s} \tag{6.22}$$

The value of the breakdown torque is determined by the total leakage reactance X, and the slip at which it occurs is determined by the rotor resistance R'_2. Figure 6.15 shows a family of torque/speed curves for different values of R'_2, and it will be seen that increasing the rotor resistance increases the standstill

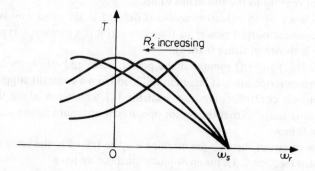

Figure 6.15   Torque/speed characteristics for varying R'_2

torque (the torque when the rotor is stationary). Unfortunately this also detracts from the full-load performance, for the following reason. At small values of slip, R'_2/s is very much greater than X, and eqn (6.19) becomes

$$T = \frac{mpV_1^2}{\omega} \cdot \frac{s}{R'_2} \qquad (6.23)$$

Thus the torque/slip characteristic is linear in this region, with a slope inversely proportional to R'_2. Equation (6.23) also shows that s must increase in proportion to R'_2 if the machine is to develop the same full-load torque. The choice of R'_2 therefore involves a compromise between the starting torque and the full-load slip, which in turn affects the efficiency and the speed regulation.

Current, power factor and efficiency

The form of the equivalent circuit (figure 6.12) shows that each phase of an induction motor will act as an inductive impedance, and the machine therefore takes current at a lagging power factor. Since the rotor impedance $R'_2/s + jx'_2$ varies in magnitude and phase angle with the slip s, the stator current I_1 will also vary with slip (and hence with the rotor speed ω_r). Figures 6.16(b) and 6.16(c) show the variation of the stator current magnitude I_1 and the power factor $\cos\phi$ (where ϕ is the phase angle between V_1 and I_1) for a typical small cage induction motor. The full-load speed is shown in the figure, and it will be seen that the starting current when the rotor is stationary is about 5 times as large as the full-load running current. Induction motors are frequently started simply by connecting the stator directly to the supply (direct-on-line or DOL starting). When the resulting high starting current is unacceptable, the phase voltage can be reduced either by the use of auto-transformers or series reactors, or by using star connection of the windings for starting and changing over to delta connection after the rotor has accelerated. For small motors, power electronic controllers can provide a 'soft start' by gradually increasing the applied voltage from zero up to the full mains value.

The efficiency of an induction motor is defined in the usual way as the ratio of the mechanical output power to the electrical input power. A typical efficiency curve is shown in figure 6.16(d).

Figure 6.16(c) and (d) show that the power factor and efficiency can be low when the motor is operating at less than full load from a constant supply voltage. Power electronic controllers are now available [1] which can adjust the supply voltage automatically so that the motor operates at optimum power factor under all load conditions.

The flow of power through the machine may be traced in the same way as for the DC motor (section 2.3); for an m-phase machine we have

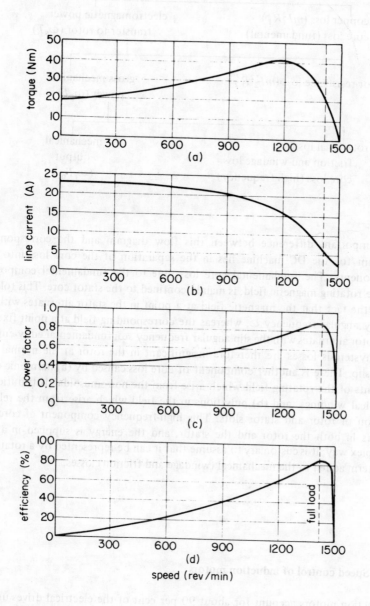

Figure 6.16 Characteristics of a typical 3 kW cage induction motor: (a) torque, (b) line current, (c) power factor, (d) efficiency

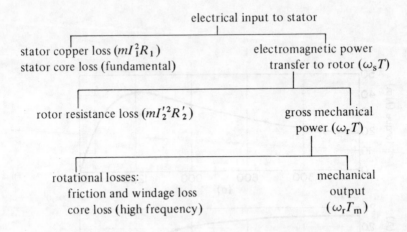

The important difference between this flow diagram and the corresponding diagram for the DC machine lies in the separation of the core loss into two components. The fundamental core loss, due to the fundamental component of the rotating magnetic field, is mainly confined to the stator core. This follows from the fact that the magnetic field at a point in the stator alternates with the supply angular frequency ω, whereas the corresponding field at a point fixed in the rotor alternates with the slip angular frequency $s\omega$; fundamental eddy-current and hysteresis losses are therefore insignificant in the rotor at the normal full-load slip. There is another component of core loss caused by (a) harmonic components of the rotating field which arise from the non-sinusoidal distribution of practical windings, and (b) pulsations in the field which arise from the relative motion of rotor and stator slots. This high-frequency component of core loss occurs in both the rotor and the stator, and the energy is supplied in a very complex way; it is customary to assume that it can be represented by a rotational loss term added to the mechanical (windage and friction) losses.

6.5 Speed control of induction motors

Induction motors account for about 90 per cent of the electrical drives used in industry, and the majority of these applications require a fairly constant speed. Induction machines are normally designed to work with a small value of slip (generally less than 5 per cent) at full load, and the deviation of the rotor speed

ω_r from the synchronous speed ω_s is therefore small. There are certain applications, however, which require substantial variation of the motor speed. DC motors form an obvious choice for this kind of drive because of the ease of speed control, but they are relatively expensive. The induction motor has the advantages of low cost and high reliability, and the possibility of controlling its speed is now examined.

The possible methods of speed control may be deduced from eqn (6.12), which defines the fractional slip s. Thus

$$\omega_r = (1 - s)\omega_s = (1 - s)\,\frac{\omega}{p} \tag{6.24}$$

showing that the rotor speed may be controlled by varying the slip s, the number of pole-pairs p, or the supply angular frequency ω. Frequency variation is the most important method, which is discussed in chapter 8. The other methods are described below.

Variation of rotor slip

For a given load torque T, eqn (6.20) shows that the quantity sX/R_2' is a constant. Increasing the resistance R_2' will cause a proportionate increase in the slip s, with a consequent decrease in the rotor speed. In practice the load torque will vary with the speed, and the precise effect of varying R_2' may be found by plotting the torque/speed characteristic for the load on the graph of motor torque/speed characteristics shown in figure 6.15. The point of intersection of the load curve with the motor characteristic gives the speed for each value of R_2', as shown in figure 6.17. Because of the power loss associated with the slip, this is an inefficient method of speed control. It is often used for short periods when a large starting torque is required; a slipring motor is employed, and the external resistance is reduced to zero as the rotor runs up to speed. When continuous operation at high slip is required for speed control purposes, the slip power can be extracted from the rotor circuit and returned to the mains via a frequency converter; this is the basis of the slip power recovery or Kramer system [2, 3]. An alternative method of varying the slip, which may be applied to cage rotor machines, is to vary the magnitude of the stator voltage V_1. Figure 6.18 shows the family of torque/speed characteristics for a number of values of V_1, and the points of intersection with the load curve give the corresponding values of speed. As with rotor resistance variation, this is an inefficient method of speed control. It has the merit of simplicity, and it is sometimes used with small machines when efficiency is not particularly important.

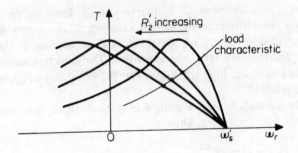

Figure 6.17   Speed control by variation of rotor resistance

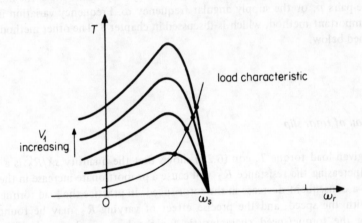

Figure 6.18   Speed control by variation of supply voltage

Pole-change windings

The second method of speed control is by alteration of the number of pole-pairs p; this can only give discrete changes of speed, since p must be an integer. With a properly designed cage rotor it is only necessary to alter the number of poles of the stator winding, for the corresponding rotor currents will find their own paths in the cage. An obvious way of varying p is to have an independent winding for each pole number, with a selector switch to connect the appropriate winding to the supply. A better solution is to design a single winding in such a way that the number of poles can be changed merely by altering the interconnection of the coils. The technique of pole-amplitude modulation [4] permits values of p such as 4, 5, 6 to be obtained from a single stator winding, which gives a useful degree of speed control.

6.6 Single-phase induction motors

Large induction motors have three-phase stator windings, and many small industrial induction motors are also made this way. Light industrial and domestic
applications require a different kind of induction motor which can operate from
a single-phase supply [5, 6]. One approach is to use a two-phase machine, with a
capacitor connected in series with one phase of the stator winding (figure 6.19).
The current I_a in the phase connected directly to the supply will lag the supply
voltage V by an angle α (figure 6.20). By a suitable choice of the capacitance
value, the current I_β in the other phase can be made to lead the voltage V by an
angle β. If $\alpha + \beta = \pi/2$, the currents are in quadrature, and the motor will operate
as a normal two-phase machine. Since the impedance presented by each phase
of the stator winding varies with the load on the motor, the phase splitting will
only be exact for one particular value of load torque, and there will be some
unbalance between the phases at other load conditions. Machines of this kind are
known as capacitor motors.

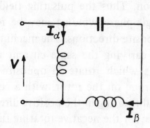

Figure 6.19   Single-phase capacitor motor

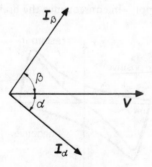

Figure 6.20   Phasor diagram for the capacitor motor

An alternative approach is to take a machine with a normal cage rotor, but only a single stator winding connected to the single-phase supply. If a current i flows in this winding, the current density is given by eqn (4.12)

$$K = -Zi \sin \theta$$

Since i is a sinusoidal alternating quantity of the form

$$i = I_m \cos \omega t$$

the current density is

$$K = -ZI_m \cos \omega t \sin \theta \qquad (6.27)$$

By a trigonometric identity this may be written in the form

$$K = -ZI_m \tfrac{1}{2}\{\sin(\omega t - \theta) + \sin(\omega t + \theta)\} \qquad (6.28)$$
$$\qquad\qquad\text{(a)}\qquad\qquad\qquad\text{(b)}$$

Term (a) in eqn (6.28) represents a field rotating with angular velocity ω in the positive direction; while term (b) represents a field rotating with angular velocity ω in the negative direction. Thus the pulsating field produced by alternating current flowing in a single-phase winding may be resolved into two rotating fields which rotate in opposite directions. The machine behaves as though it had two polyphase windings, carrying the same current magnitude per phase, but producing magnetic fields which rotate in opposite directions. Each rotating field will give rise to a torque on the rotor, with a corresponding torque/speed characteristic. For the field rotating in the positive direction, this is similar to the normal torque/speed curve; for the negative rotating field the direction of torque is reversed, and zero slip now corresponds to a rotor speed of $-\omega_s$. Figure 6.21 shows the two torque/speed curves, together with the resultant torque which is the sum of the two components. The torque characteristic for each component field is somewhat different from the normal torque/speed characteristic, because the EMF induced by the other field component affects the current which the stator draws from the supply. In consequence the braking torque is reduced, and

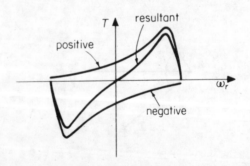

Figure 6.21   Torque/speed characteristic for a single-winding single-phase motor

the net output torque is greater than would be given by the normal torque/speed characteristics: see problem 6.6.

The resultant torque is zero when the rotor is stationary, so the machine is not inherently self-starting. If some means is provided for spinning the rotor, the resultant torque acts in a direction to accelerate the rotor, which will run up to speed in the normal way. The starting torque is provided by an auxiliary winding in space quadrature with the main winding; the field produced by this winding combines with a portion of the main field to produce a rotating field, which exerts a torque on the stationary rotor. There are three common arrangements for the auxiliary winding.

Shaded-pole motor

This simple form of single-phase motor is shown in figure 6.22. The stator has salient poles carrying the main winding, and a portion of each pole is enclosed by a ring which is usually made of copper. Currents are induced in the ring (or 'shading coil') by the alternating magnetic field, and the portion of the pole enclosed by the ring is 'shaded' from the main pole flux; the flux is weaker, and its phase is retarded relative to the main flux. The arrangement forms a rudimentary two-phase winding which is adequate for accelerating the rotor against light loads. Motors of this kind are robust and inexpensive; but they are also inefficient, and their use is restricted to sizes below about 250 W.

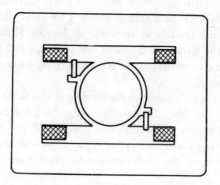

Figure 6.22 Shaded-pole induction motor

Split-phase motor

For larger sizes of single-phase induction motor (up to about 1 kW) with modest starting torque requirements, a normal stator construction is used. The auxiliary winding is designed to have very different values of resistance and reactance from the main winding, so that there is an appreciable phase shift between the currents when the two windings are connected to the same single-phase supply. Thus the phase-splitting is inherent in the machine design, and the auxiliary winding normally has a short time rating. It is disconnected once the rotor has run up to speed, either by a centrifugally operated switch or by a relay which senses when the main winding current has fallen from a high starting value to the normal running value.

Capacitor-start motor

When the motor must develop a large starting torque, the capacitor motor arrangement is used. This gives a larger phase angle between the main and auxiliary currents (ideally 90°), and permits a better design of the auxiliary winding since the phase shift is provided by the capacitor. As with the split-phase motor, the auxiliary winding is disconnected once the rotor has run up to speed. The capacitor is usually an AC electrolytic type with a short time rating; this is much cheaper than the type of capacitor required for continuous operation in a capacitor motor.

Applications

Single-phase induction motors have lower values of efficiency and power factor than comparable polyphase machines, and their use is restricted to powers below about 4 kW. The majority have ratings below 1 kW, and they are employed in very large numbers, particularly in domestic appliances. Shaded-pole motors are used for small fan and pump drives and in low-cost tape and record decks. Split-phase or capacitor-start motors are often used in refrigerators, washing machines and small machine tools.

Motors which run with a single main winding suffer from two disadvantages: the power factor is low; and the pulsating magnetic field causes the torque to pulsate at twice the supply frequency, which may result in noise and vibration. If the motor has to run continuously for long periods, or if noise is a problem, it may be preferable to use the more expensive capacitor motor.

6.7 Linear induction motors

The induction-motor principle can be made to produce linear motion by the simple expedient of placing the stator coils in a flat iron core instead of a cylindrical core. Three-phase currents flowing in the stator, or primary, coils will produce a current-density pattern which travels along the surface; this will set up a travelling magnetic field analogous to the rotating magnetic field in a rotary induction motor. If a flat conducting plate is placed next to the primary, the field will induce currents in the plate, and the interaction of these currents with the field will produce a force tending to move the plate in the direction of motion of the field. The plate usually has an iron backing to complete the magnetic circuit, and it is the linear counterpart of the rotor of a conventional motor; it is termed the *secondary*. If the secondary were made the same length as the primary, then the two would soon separate; consequently linear induction motors are made in two forms: short-primary machines and short-secondary machines (figure 6.23). These are the most common forms of linear induction motor, but several other arrangements are possible [6, 7, 8].

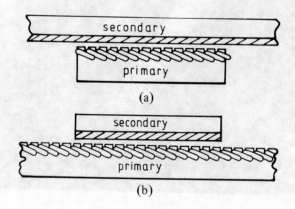

(a)

(b)

Figure 6.23   Linear induction motors: (a) short primary; (b) short secondary

Linear induction motors differ from rotary machines in two important respects. Firstly, the airgap is usually much larger; this entails a large magnetising current, and in consequence the power factor and efficiency are low. Secondly, the magnetic field decays at the ends of the primary; in a rotary machine, the rotating field closes on itself and is effectively endless. In a short-primary machine, currents in the secondary are largely confined to the region of the primary; currents have to build up as secondary material approaches the entry edge, and then decay as material leaves the exit edge. These transient currents set up field components travelling at different speeds from the primary current wave, and they modify the performance of the machine in a complex way [4, 7, 9]. The effects depend on the slip; they result in a reduction of the force on the secondary and an increase in the losses.

Applications of linear induction motors are numerous [6, 8, 10]. Industrial uses include the propulsion of overhead travelling cranes and the handling of sheet metals such as aluminium. They are widely proposed for advanced ground transport systems [10, 11]; several prototype systems have been demonstrated, and figure 6.24 shows the stator of a linear motor for a low-speed passenger vehicle which has been in commercial service in Birmingham since 1984 [10, 12, 13].

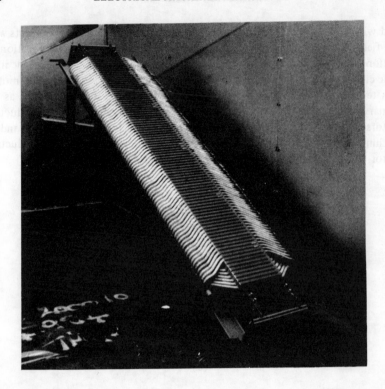

Figure 6.24 Primary of a linear induction motor for a passenger vehicle (Brush Electrical Machines Ltd)

Problems

6.1. In problem 2.3, the DC shunt motor is replaced by a slipring induction motor with an external resistance R in each phase of the rotor circuit. If the internal losses of the motor may be neglected, show that the same expressions hold for the hoisting speed and the efficiency.

6.2. If the stator of an induction motor is supplied with a constant current I_1, and the rotor leakage reactance may be neglected, obtain an expression for the torque in a form similar to eqn (6.20). If s_m is the slip for maximum torque, compare the values of s_m for constant-current and constant-voltage operation.

6.3. A cage induction motor has direct current applied to the stator winding. Show that the machine acts as a brake for both directions of rotation, and deduce the shape of the torque/speed curve by considering the slip speed of an induction motor operating from a constant-current AC supply.

6.4. When the rotor of an induction motor accelerates from rest with no mechanical load coupled to the shaft, part of the energy input to the rotor will be dissipated as heat in the rotor resistance and part will be stored as kinetic energy of the rotor. If rotational losses may be neglected, show that when the rotor reaches the synchronous speed the total energy dissipated in the rotor resistance is equal to the final kinetic energy of the rotor.

6.5. An induction motor has a two-phase stator winding, and it runs with a slip s when positive-sequence voltages V_p and $-jV_p$ are applied to the α and β phases respectively. With the rotor speed unchanged the positive-sequence supply is disconnected and negative-sequence voltages V_n, jV_n are applied to the α and β phases respectively. Show that the slip is now equal to $2 - s$, and draw complete equivalent circuits for the two conditions of operation.

6.6. In problem 6.5, the voltages V_p and V_n are adjusted so that in the first case the α and β phase currents are I, $-jI$ and in the second they are I, jI. Use the principle of superposition to show that the motor operates as a single-phase machine when voltages $(V_p + V_n)$, $(-jV_p + jV_n)$ are applied to the α and β phases respectively, and hence combine the two separate equivalent circuits into a single equivalent circuit for the single-phase machine. Note that the currents in a circuit will be doubled if all the impedance values are halved.

References

1 L. Holmes, 'Energy-saving motor controllers', *Electronics and Power*, **28** (1982), pp. 232-5.

2 A. E. Fitzgerald, C. Kingsley Jr. and S. D. Umans, *Electric Machinery*, 4th ed. (New York: McGraw-Hill, 1983).

3 D. Finney, *Variable Frequency AC Motor Drive Systems* (London: Peter Peregrinus, 1988).

4 B. V. Jayawant, *Induction Machines* (Maidenhead: McGraw-Hill, 1968).

5 P. L. Alger, *Induction Machines*, 2nd ed. (New York: Gordon and Breach, 1970).

6 M. G. Say, *Alternating Current Machines*, 5th ed. (London: Pitman, 1983).

7 E. R. Laithwaite, *Induction Machines for Special Purposes* (London: Newnes, 1966).

8 E. R. Laithwaite, *Linear Electric Motors* (London: Mills and Boon, 1971).

9 S. Yamamura, *Theory of Linear Induction Motors*, 2nd ed. (University of Tokyo Press, 1978).

10 G. W. McLean, 'Review of recent progress in linear motors', *IEE Proc. B, Electr. Power Appl.*, **135** (1988), pp. 380-416.

11 B. V. Jayawant, *Electromagnetic Suspension and Levitation Techniques* (London: Edward Arnold, 1981).

12 H. Linacre, J. S. Chahal, G. Crawshaw and B. Rawlinson, 'Birmingham Airport maglev propulsion system', *IMechE International Conference on Maglev Transport, October 1984, C408/84*, pp. 193-201.

13 D. A. Bradley, *Power Electronics* (Wokingham: Van Nostrand Reinhold (UK), 1987).

7 DC Drive Systems

7.1 Introduction

In section 2.5 we have seen that the speed of a classical DC motor is easily controlled by varying the voltage applied to the armature; but available power sources – mains or batteries – are essentially fixed voltage. Techniques of power electronics enable a variable voltage to be derived from one of these sources; the combination of an electronic controller with a DC motor makes a most effective variable-speed drive system. This system has dominated the market for two decades, but it now faces serious competition from the AC variable-frequency systems discussed in chapter 8 and the new electronically commutated machines described in chapter 10.

Power electronic controllers fall into two main groups: (a) AC/DC converters, where a unidirectional voltage is derived from the AC mains by phase-controlled rectification using thyristors; (b) chopper controllers, where transistors or thyristors switch a DC supply on and off alternately, thereby controlling the mean voltage applied to the motor. Both types of controller allow the mean voltage to be varied over a wide range, with a corresponding range of speed variation.

The operating principles of these controllers are described in sections 7.3 and 7.4. In keeping with the general aims of this book, the treatment concentrates on the functional principles and ignores those technological aspects which are the province of the power electronics designer. The presentation therefore omits topics such as device characteristics, driving methods, and device protection; these will be found in specialist texts such as Williams [1] and Thorborg [2].

All the power electronic controllers covered in this book have one feature in common: the power semiconductor devices are used as electrically controlled switches that are either open or closed. The power loss in the switch itself is ideally zero, since there is no current flowing when it is open, and no potential difference when it is closed. A power electronic controller therefore has high efficiency – it would be 100 per cent if the devices were perfect. This is fundamentally different from a linear amplifier, where the circuit operation requires both a current through the device and a potential difference across it; there may be more power dissipated in the amplifier than in the load which it supplies.

7.2 Power semiconductor devices

The ideal power switch would have infinite resistance when open and zero resistance when closed; it would change from one state to the other in zero time, and require zero control power to change its state. Practical semiconductor devices all depart from this ideal to a greater or lesser extent. This section gives a brief survey of the common power devices only to the extent necessary to understand the principles of the basic power conversion circuits.

Rectifier diode

The normal p-n junction diode will conduct current when a forward voltage is applied, making the anode positive with respect to cathode. It will block current when a reverse voltage is applied, making the anode negative with respect to cathode. The forward voltage is about 0.7 V when the diode begins to conduct, rising to about 1 V when the full rated current is flowing. For reverse voltages up to the *reverse breakdown value*, only a small leakage current will flow; this is typically one millionth of the rated forward current.

A diode acts as an automatic switch, which is closed when a forward voltage is applied and open when a reverse voltage is applied.

Thyristor (SCR)

The thyristor or silicon controlled rectifier (SCR) is a four-layer p-n-p-n device, with a gate terminal connected to the intermediate p-layer. It behaves like a rectifier diode in which the forward conduction is controlled by the gate. With a reverse voltage applied, the characteristic is similar to that of a diode. When a forward voltage is applied, the behaviour depends on the gate current in the following way.

In the absence of gate current, a forward voltage will cause only a small leakage current to flow, provided that the voltage is less than the *forward breakover value*. If this value is exceeded, the thyristor switches to a conducting state resembling the forward conduction of a diode; the forward voltage drop is then about 2 V. The thryristor remains in a conducting state until the current falls below the *holding current*; if this condition persists for long enough, the thyristor reverts to a forward blocking state.

If current is injected into the gate, by making it positive with respect to the cathode, the thyristor will switch from a forward blocking state to a conducting state at a much lower voltage. Once the thyristor is conducting, the gate has no further effect on the forward current; removing the gate current will not make the thyristor turn off. The only way to turn it off is to reduce the forward current to a value below the holding current.

In practice the thyristor is operated with a forward voltage below the forward breakover value; it is then effectively non-conducting until a pulse of gate current causes it to switch to the conducting state. It is turned off when the external circuit reduces the current to zero; normally the circuit also applies a reverse voltage to speed up the turn-off process. The process of turning on the thyristor by applying a pulse to the gate is termed *firing* or *triggering*. Gate firing circuits usually apply a train of pulses to ensure that the thyristor turns on with an inductive load; with only a single firing pulse, the load current may not reach the holding value before the end of the pulse.

A useful feature of the thyristor is its capacity for withstanding brief current overloads. The internal turn-on mechanism is inherently self-sustaining, so that a large current causes the device to turn on harder; this is quite different from the overload behaviour of the power transistor described below.

Thyristors have slower switching speeds than transistors, and often require special commutation circuits to switch them off; but they are unrivalled for high-power applications, since they are available with much higher voltage and current ratings than transistors.

Gate turn-off thyristor (GTO)

The gate turn-off thyristor (GTO) overcomes the turn-off problem of the thyristor by permitting the forward current to be turned off with a negative gate current. Unlike the conventional thyristor, the GTO requires a continuous positive gate current to maintain a forward conducting state reliably.

GTOs combine the power-handling capacity of the thyristor with the control capability of the transistor; they have an important role in high-power inverters (see chapter 8).

Power transistor

The bipolar junction power transistor is normally a three-layer n-p-n device, which is controlled by the current in the base p-layer. For switching applications, the collector–emitter characteristics are controlled by the base current as follows. When the base current is zero, the transistor is *cut off*; only a small leakage current will flow from collector to emitter for voltages less than the *forward breakdown* value. When the base is made positive with respect to the emitter, so that positive base current I_b flows, the transistor will be *saturated* as long as the collector current I_c is less than βI_b, where β is the current gain. The collector–emitter voltage then has a low value known as the *saturation voltage*.

In any given switching circuit, the transistor must be kept saturated for all values of collector current by driving sufficient current into the base. If the transistor comes out of saturation, then the combination of high collector current and high collector–emitter voltage will result in a destructive dissipation of power in the device. The transistor thus differs fundamentally from the thyristor in its ability to handle current overloads.

Power MOSFET

In a MOSFET (metal–oxide–semiconductor field-effect transistor), the flow of current in a semiconductor channel is controlled by the voltage applied to a gate electrode which is electrically insulated from the channel. No gate current is required in the steady state, but current must flow transiently to charge and discharge the gate capacitance. The normal power MOSFET is an n-channel enhancement mode device; it is non-conducting until the gate–source voltage reaches a positive *threshold voltage*. For gate–source voltages above this value the channel between the drain and the source becomes highly conductive, and behaves as a pure resistance as long as the drain–source voltage is small. The power MOSFET thus behaves as a voltage-controlled switch with a high off-state resistance and a low on-state resistance. It is capable of very high switching speeds, and it requires much less drive power than a bipolar junction power transistor. Power MOSFETs are easier to operate in parallel for increased current capacity, and they do not exhibit the second breakdown phenomenon which can destroy power transistors. Unfortunately they are more limited in their voltage and current ratings, because a high voltage rating entails a disproportionate increase in the on-state resistance.

Insulated-gate bipolar transistor (IGBT)

The IGBT attempts to combine the best properties of the bipolar transistor and the MOSFET. The ideal device has the gate of an FET and the collector–emitter structure of a transistor. In reality the device is formed by integrating a circuit such as the cascode connection of a transistor and a MOSFET [2]. These IGBTs can be controlled in the same way as MOSFETs; they have high switching speeds and high voltage capability. At present they are mainly confined to low power applications, for example motor drives below 20 kW.

7.3 AC/DC converters

AC/DC converters are circuits which convert alternating current or voltage into direct current or voltage. The simplest circuits are rectifiers which use only diodes; the resulting DC output is then determined by the amplitude of the AC supply input. Control of the DC output is made possible by replacing some or all of the diodes with controlled switches. In this application the thyristor is the normal choice for a controlled switch, because the periodic reversal of the AC input automatically turns the device off; the converter is said to be *naturally commutated*.

There are many different configurations of converter circuits, which are described in texts such as Lander [3] and Bird and King [4]. Those which are most generally used are the bridge circuits with single-phase or three-phase inputs. They normally supply loads which have significant inductance as well as resistance; the load may also include a source of EMF such as a DC machine armature. This section begins by describing the basic converter operation with a passive load, in which there is no source of EMF; the effect of an active load is considered at the end of the section.

Single-phase bridge converter

Uncontrolled converter

Figure 7.1 shows a single-phase bridge rectifier circuit using four diodes; it is an uncontrolled converter. During one half-cycle of the AC supply, diodes D_1 and D_4 conduct; during the next half-cycle, D_2 and D_3 conduct. The effect of the diodes is to reverse the connections of the load to the supply every half cycle, so that the load voltage v_L is unidirectional as shown in figure 7.2(a). Notice that the diodes switch over at every zero crossing of the supply voltage waveform.

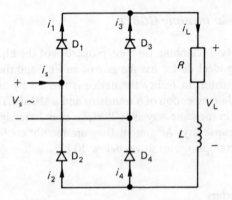

Figure 7.1   Single-phase bridge rectifier circuit

The load inductance will have a smoothing effect on the current, so that the load current does not follow the shape of the voltage waveform. If the load time-constant L/R is large in comparison with the period of the AC supply, then the load current will be nearly constant. For simplicity we shall ignore any variation in the load current; the currents in the diodes are then rectangular pulses, as shown in figures 7.2(b) and 7.2(c). The resulting current i_s in the supply lines is a square wave as shown in figure 7.2(d).

It has been assumed that current will switch instantaneously from one pair of diodes to the other. In practice there will be some inductance in the AC supply

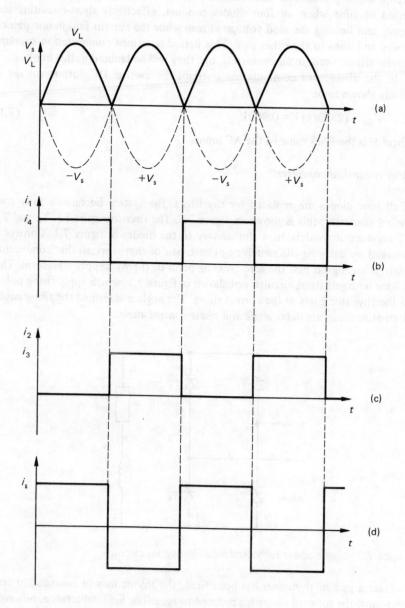

Figure 7.2 Waveforms for the single-phase bridge rectifier

circuit which prevents an instantaneous change. Consequently there will be a period of time when all four diodes conduct, effectively short-circuiting the supply and holding the load voltage at zero while the current falls in one pair of diodes and rises in the other pair. This period is termed *commutation overlap*. Similar effects occur in all converters, but they will be ignored in this book.

In the absence of commutation overlap, the average DC output voltage is readily shown to be

$$V_{do} = (2\sqrt{2}/\pi)V = 0.900V \tag{7.1}$$

where V is the RMS value of the AC input.

Fully controlled converter

If all four diodes are replaced by thyristors, the system becomes a fully controlled converter; this is shown in figure 7.3. The thyristor pairs T_1, T_4 and T_2, T_3 conduct alternately in a similar way to the diodes in figure 7.1. Control is achieved by delaying the switching of each pair of thyristors, so that conduction starts at an angle α past the zero-crossing point of the AC supply waveform. This is done with gate firing circuits, not shown in figure 7.3, which apply firing pulses to the thyristor gates at the correct times. The angle α is termed the *firing angle*; alternative terms are *delay angle* and *phase control angle*.

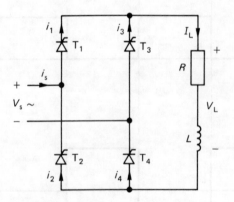

Figure 7.3   Single-phase fully controlled converter circuit

Once a pair of thyristors has been fired, the thyristors will continue to conduct until the forward current is reduced to zero. The load inductance, however, will tend to maintain a constant current in the thyristors; they will not turn off until the other two are fired. Because this firing point is delayed by an angle α past the zero crossing, the load voltage v_L will go negative for part of the time, as shown in figure 7.4(a). The average value of the load voltage thus depends on the angle α, and is given by

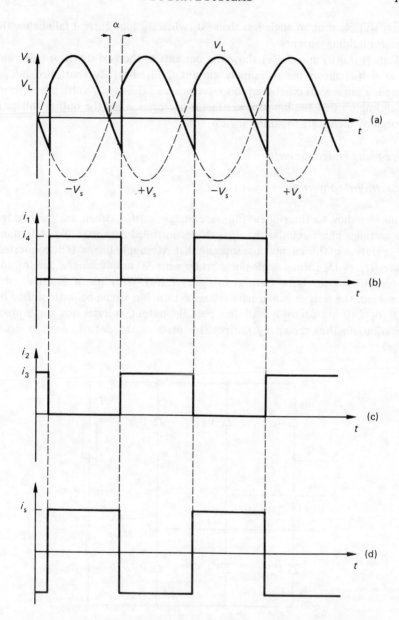

Figure 7.4 Waveforms for the single-phase fully controlled converter

$$V_d = V_{d0} \cos \alpha$$

where V_{d0} is the output of an uncontrolled converter given by eqn (7.1). The average output voltage approaches zero as α approaches $90°$, but converter action will cease at an angle less than 90° when the load current falls below the thyristor holding current.

Figures 7.4(b) and 7.4(c) show the currents in the two thyristor pairs, and figure 7.4(d) shows the AC supply current i_s for the fully controlled bridge. There is a phase shift α between this waveform and the supply voltage waveform, which implies that the input power factor decreases when the output voltage is reduced by increasing the firing angle α.

Three-phase bridge converter

Uncontrolled converter

Figure 7.5 shows a three-phase full-wave bridge rectifier circuit using six diodes; like its single-phase counterpart, it is an uncontrolled converter. To understand the operation of this circuit, first suppose that AC supply line 'c' is disconnected. Diodes D_1 to D_4 form a single-phase bridge with AC supply lines 'a' and 'b', and the output has the same form as in figure 7.2(a). With line 'a' or line 'b' disconnected, the output would have the same form but would be phase-shifted by 120° or 240° respectively. All the possible output voltages for single-phase operation are thus shown by the positive parts of the dotted curves in figure 7.6(a).

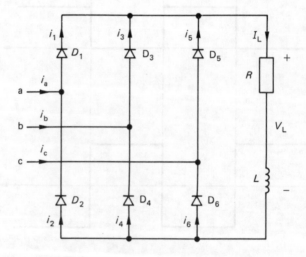

Figure 7.5   Three-phase bridge rectifier circuit

When all three AC supply lines are connected, the output voltage follows the solid curve in figure 7.6(a). Diodes conduct in sequence so that, at any instant, the load is connected to the pair of supply lines with the largest voltage. Suppose,

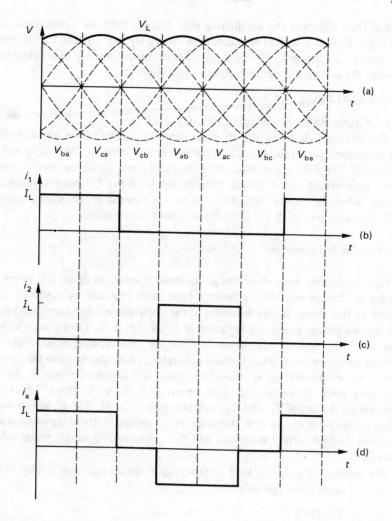

Figure 7.6 Waveforms for the three-phase bridge rectifier

for instance, that diodes D_1 and D_4 are conducting, thus connecting lines 'a' and 'b' to the load. The voltage v_{ab} will pass its peak and start to decrease; meanwhile the voltage v_{ac} between lines 'a' and 'c' will increase towards its peak. When v_{ac} exceeds v_{ab}, diode D_6 begins to conduct; the voltage across diode D_4 reverses, and it ceases to conduct. This process continues cyclically, with the conducting path switching from one diode to another every 60°. The pattern of conducting diodes is as follows, for successive 60° intervals:

$$
\begin{array}{llllllll}
D_1 & D_1 & D_3 & D_3 & D_5 & D_5 & D_1 & \ldots \\
D_4 & D_6 & D_6 & D_2 & D_2 & D_4 & D_4 & \ldots
\end{array}
$$

Notice that, although the conducting path changes every 60°, each diode conducts for 120° at a time. The currents in diodes D_1 and D_2, and the current in AC line 'a', are shown in figures 7.6(b)-7.6(d). In the absence of commutation overlap, the average DC output voltage is given by

$$V_{d0} = (3\sqrt{2}/\pi)\,V = 1.35\,V \tag{7.3}$$

where V is the RMS line voltage of the AC supply.

This circuit is classified as a six-pulse converter because there are six switching transitions per cycle and six ripple pulses per cycle in the output voltage waveform. The principal advantage of the three-phase converter over its single-phase counterpart is the greatly reduced ripple in the DC output voltage. A further advantage is the elimination of triplen harmonics (harmonic numbers which are multiples of three) from the line current waveform.

Fully controlled converter

A fully controlled three-phase bridge converter is shown in figure 7.7, where the diodes of the uncontrolled converter have been replaced by thyristors. The action of this circuit is similar to that of the single-phase fully controlled bridge; the output voltage waveform is shown in figure 7.8(a) for a firing angle α. Note that the firing angle is not measured from the zero crossing point of the line voltage waveform, as in a single-phase converter; it is measured from the point at which a forward voltage is developed across the thyristor, which is also the switching point of an uncontrolled converter, as shown in figure 7.8(a). The currents in thyristors T_1 and T_2, and the current in AC line 'a', are shown in figures 7.8(b)-7.8(d). As with the single-phase converter, there is a phase shift α between the line current waveform and the corresponding supply phase voltage waveform.

The average value of the load voltage is given by an equation similar to eqn (7.2) for a single-phase converter:

$$V_d = V_{d0}\cos\alpha \tag{7.4}$$

where V_{d0} is the output of an uncontrolled converter given by eqn (7.3).

Half-controlled bridge converter

Control of the converter output voltage is still possible if only half the diodes are replaced by thyristors – usually D_1 and D_3 in a single-phase bridge, and D_1, D_3 and D_5 in a three-phase bridge. In addition, a *free-wheeling* or *commutating* diode is usually connected in parallel with the load, to prevent the load voltage from going negative and to provide a return path for the load current when the thyristors are turned off. These half-controlled converters are cheaper than fully-controlled converters, but the AC supply waveform is more distorted, and the output of a three-phase bridge has a higher ripple content. They will not be considered further in this book.

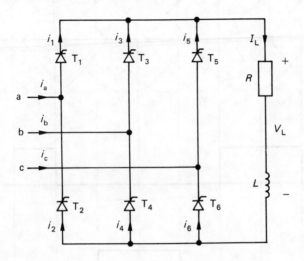

Figure 7.7   Three-phase fully controlled converter circuit

Active load

If the load is active – which means that it contains a source of EMF such as a battery or a DC motor armature – its effect on the converter will depend on whether the EMF aids or opposes the converter output voltage. If it opposes the output, then the load current will be reduced to zero when the mean voltage is equal to the EMF; this will occur when the firing angle α is less than $90°$. If the EMF aids the output, then a different kind of converter action is possible.

Inverter action

If the load EMF acts in the same direction as the output voltage of a fully controlled converter, then the load current will continue to flow when the firing angle α is $90°$ and the mean output voltage is zero. Any further increase in the firing angle will make the mean output voltage negative, and the flow of power will reverse; the load will supply power to the converter, which in turn will transfer the power to the AC source. The source current will then have a component in antiphase with the voltage. When the power flow reverses in this way, the converter is said to be operating in the *inverting mode*.

In the fully controlled converter, power can flow in either direction, but current can only slow in one direction: from the converter to the load. The

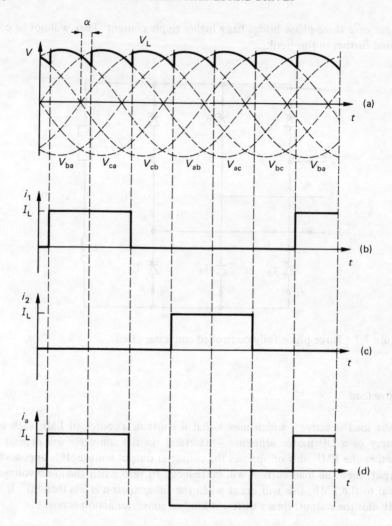

Figure 7.8   Waveforms for the three-phase fully controlled converter

direction of power flow is determined by the firing angle, which controls the magnitude and sign of the output voltage.

Discontinuous current

If the load inductance is small, so that it is no longer true that the L/R time constant is much greater than the period of the AC supply, then the load current will not be constant. In this case it is possible for the load current to fall to zero before the next thyristor pair is triggered, resulting in discontinuous load current.

If the load includes a source of EMF which opposes the output voltage, then the voltage across the load inductance will reverse when the converter output voltage is less than the EMF. This will cause a more rapid fall in the load current which may result in discontinuous current, even though the current is continuous with a passive load. The effect becomes more pronounced when the EMF is nearly equal to the average output voltage of the converter.

7.4 DC choppers

Choppers operate from a constant DC source, and deliver a controllable voltage to the load. The basic principle of a chopper circuit is shown in figure 7.9; it consists of a controlled switch S in series between the source and the load, and a diode in parallel with the load. When the switch S is opened and closed periodically, the load voltage has the rectangular waveform shown in figure 7.10. If the switch is closed for a time t_1 and open for a time t_2, the average load voltage is given by

$$v_L = (t_1/T)V_s$$

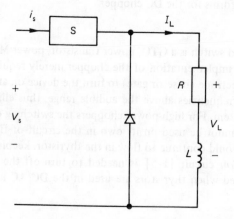

Figure 7.9   Basic DC chopper circuit

where $T = t_1 + t_2$ is the period of the waveform, and V_s is the DC supply voltage; the ratio t_1/T is known as the duty cycle. The *freewheeling diode* is an essential part of the chopper; it provides a path for the load current when the switch is open. As with an AC/DC converter, load inductance will tend to maintain a constant load current. This current flows in the supply lines when the switch is closed, and in the diode when the switch is open; the supply current waveform therefore takes the form shown in figure 7.10.

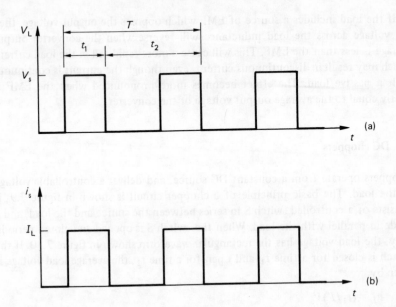

Figure 7.10   Waveforms for the DC chopper

If the controlled switch is a GTO, power transistor, power MOSFET or IGBT, then the practical implementation of the chopper merely requires a drive circuit for the control electrode (base or gate) to turn the device on and off. MOSFETs permit switching frequencies above the audible range, thus eliminating acoustic noise from the system. For high-power choppers the switching element is usually a thyristor; this cannot be used on its own in the circuit of figure 7.9, because the load current would continue to flow in the thyristor, keeping it turned on. A *forced commutation* circuit [1–5] is needed to turn off the thyristor. Similar circuits are required when thyristors are used in the DC/AC inverters described in chapter 8.

7.5 DC drive system performance

Motor speed control

In most DC variable-speed drive systems the DC motor is controlled by varying the armature voltage; a constant field flux is provided by permanent magnets in small machines, or a constant field current in large machines. For a given controller output voltage V_a applied to the armature, the motor speed/torque characteristic is given by

$$\omega = \omega_0(1 - T/T_0) \tag{2.28}$$

where ω_0 is the no-load speed given by

$$\omega_0 = V_a/(K_a\Phi) \tag{2.29}$$

and T_0 is the stall torque corresponding to the stall current I_{a0}:

$$T_0 = K_a\Phi I_{a0} \tag{2.30}$$

$$I_{a0} = V_a/R \tag{7.6}$$

where R includes the effective output resistance of the controller as well as the motor armature resistance R_a. Equation [2.28] is valid only if the motor armature current is continuous. If the current is discontinuous, which can happen with a phase-controlled converter under light-load conditions (see section 7.4), then the torque/speed characteristic becomes non-linear with much poorer speed regulation [6].

Closed-loop control

If the inherent speed regulation implied by eqn [2.28] is unacceptable, then a feedback system must be used to control the converter or chopper output voltage. Armature voltage feedback will compensate for the internal resistance of the controller, and armature current feedback can compensate approximately for the armature resistance of the motor; together they can give a speed regulation of about 2 per cent of the maximum speed over the range of no-load to full-load torque. The merit of this scheme is that it does not require separate measurement of the motor speed. If closer speed control is required, then the speed must be measured with a tachogenerator or digital transducer, and the speed signal used to regulate the controller output voltage.

Speed reversal

The direction of rotation can be reversed in three ways:

(a) by reversing the direction of the field flux;
(b) by reversing the connections to the armature;
(c) by providing a second converter in parallel with the first, but giving a voltage of the opposite polarity [3-5].

Option (a), reversal of the field flux, is possible only with a wound-field motor. The field current must first be reduced to zero and then the connections to the field winding reversed. With this method the speed of reversal is limited by the field time constant L_f/R_f, which may be greater than 1 second in a large DC motor.

Option (b), reversal of the armature connections, is suitable for all types of DC motor, and for both AC/DC converters and choppers. As with field reversal, the armature current must be reduced to zero before the connections are reversed; but this can be faster than field reversal because the armature time constant L_f/R_f is typically one tenth of the field time constant.

Option (c), the anti-parallel converter connection (double converter), achieves the same result as (b), but with three significant advantages. A contactor is not required for reversing the connections; a continuous transition from forward to reverse is possible by control of the two converters; and the torque can be reversed for dynamic braking (see below). The penalty is the cost of the second converter, which will usually have the same power rating as the first.

Torque reversal

The torque of a DC motor is given by

$$T = K_a \Phi I_a$$ [2.11]

where I_a is the armature current. If the torque is to be reversed without reversing the speed, then the direction of I_a must be reversed. This is required for dynamic braking, where the reverse torque gives rapid deceleration of the mechanical load. Current reversal cannot be achieved with a single chopper or converter, because the power semiconductor switches permit current flow in only one direction. The double converter used for speed reversal is also suitable for dynamic braking, since the second converter supplies current in the reverse direction.

Motor losses

There will be additional losses in DC motors operated from power electronic controllers. The field system is usually laminated to reduce eddy-current losses caused by flux pulsations, so the additional loss from this source is small. More serious is the additional ohmic loss in the armature winding caused by the current fluctuation, particularly if the current is discontinuous. Suppose that the armature current has a mean value I_1 and that the fluctuating component has an RMS value I_2. If the field flux is constant, the mean torque is

$$T = K_a \Phi I_1$$ (7.7)

and the armature ohmic loss is

$$P_a = (I_1^2 + I_2^2) R_a$$ (7.8)

Thus, for a given mean torque, the current fluctuation will cause an additional loss equal to $I_2^2 R_a$. In practice the loss may be higher than this because skin effect increases the effective resistance of the armature at the frequencies of the harmonic components of the pulsation. An additional loss of about 10 per cent is common with phase-controlled motors [6].

Supply system considerations

Harmonics

In section 7.3 it was shown that a converter with a highly inductive load has an AC line current waveform which is rectangular in shape. For the single-phase bridge converter, the current is a square wave with an amplitude equal to the load current I_L; the Fourier series for this waveform is

$$i_s = (4I_L/\pi) \left(\sin \omega t + \tfrac{1}{3} \sin 3\omega t + \tfrac{1}{5} \sin 5\omega t + \ldots\right) \tag{7.9}$$

The harmonic amplitudes decrease slowly with harmonic number, so single-phase converters can inject significant quantities of harmonic currents into the AC supply system. Electricity supply authorities impose limits on the levels of harmonic currents generated by the consumer [3], so single-phase converters are generally limited to power levels below 10 kW.

In a three-phase bridge converter the line current waveform is quasi-square, with periods of zero current between the positive and negative rectangles. The Fourier series is similar in form to that of a square wave, except that the triplen harmonics are absent. This type of converter is used in power levels up to about 1 MW. For higher powers, converters with 12 or more pulses per cycle are used to obtain lower harmonic current levels [3].

Power factor

When the current and voltage contain harmonics, we can no longer use the conventional definition of power factor as $\cos \phi$, where ϕ is the phase angle. The extended definition is

$$\text{power factor} = \frac{\text{mean power}}{V_{\text{RMS}} I_{\text{RMS}}} \tag{7.10}$$

which reduces to $\cos \phi$ when the current and voltage are both sinusoidal. If the voltage is sinusoidal, which is usually a good approximation, the mean power is $V_{\text{RMS}} I_{\text{1RMS}} \cos \phi_1$, where I_{1RMS} is the fundamental component of current and ϕ_1 is its phase angle with respect to the voltage. Equation (7.10) then becomes

$$\text{power factor} = \frac{I_{\text{1RMS}}}{I_{\text{RMS}}} \cos \phi_1 = \mu \cos \phi_1 \tag{7.11}$$

where $\mu = I_{\text{1RMS}}/I_{\text{RMS}}$ is the *current distortion factor*. Thus the power factor of an AC/DC converter may be less than 1, even when there is no phase shift between the fundamental components of voltage and the current. In a fully-controlled converter with constant load current, the phase angle ϕ_1 is equal to the firing angle α.

Problems

7.1. Derive eqns (7.1) and (7.2) for the DC output voltage of an uncontrolled and fully controlled single-phase bridge converter respectively.

7.2. Derive eqns (7.3) and (7.4) for the DC output voltage of an uncontrolled and fully controlled three-phase bridge converter respectively.

7.3. Determine the power factor of (a) a single-phase diode bridge, (b) a three-phase diode bridge, when the load current is constant.

References

1   B. W. Williams, *Power Electronics: Devices, Drivers and Applications* (London: Macmillan, 1987).

2   K. Thorborg, *Power Electronics* (New York: Prentice-Hall, 1988).

3   C. W. Lander, *Power Electronics*, 2nd ed. (London: McGraw-Hill, 1987).

4   B. M. Bird and K. G. King, *An Introduction to Power Electronics* (Chichester: Wiley, 1983).

5   D. A. Bradley, *Power Electronics* (Wokingham: Van Nostrand Reinhold, 1987).

6   M. G. Say and E. O. Taylor, *Direct Current Machines*, 2nd ed. (London: Pitman, 1986).

8 AC Drive Systems

8.1 Introduction

The speed of an AC motor depends on the speed of the rotating magnetic field, which is proportional to the frequency of the AC supply. Speed control is therefore possible with a power electronic controller which can generate a variable frequency. The majority of AC variable-speed drive systems use a DC/AC inverter to generate the required variable frequency from a DC source. Since the primary power source is usually the AC mains, an AC/DC converter is also required; a frequency conversion system of this kind is termed a *DC link converter*. It is also possible to convert power directly from the fixed AC supply frequency to a variable output frequency with a *cycloconverter* [1], which does not use a DC link. Converters of this kind are generally restricted to output frequencies of not more than one third of the input frequency, so they are not widely used; they will not be considered further in this book.

We have seen in chapter 4 that a three-phase sinusoidal supply is particularly suitable for AC motors; it gives a smoothly rotating magnetic field which exerts a steady torque on the rotor. The normal practice, therefore, is to use three-phase inverters for variable-speed AC drives. The usual circuit is a three-phase bridge similar to an AC/DC converter, using controlled semiconductor switches to generate an alternating output from a constant (DC) input. A circuit of this kind tends to generate a waveform which is rectangular in shape, which is not ideal for motor control; but the current can be made nearly sinusoidal by a switching technique known as *pulse-width modulation* (PWM).

There are two main categories of inverter: voltage-source and current-source. Voltage-source inverters operate from a constant DC link voltage, and generate rectangular voltage waveforms; current-source inverters operate from a constant DC link current, and generate rectangular current waveforms. An important variant of the voltage-source inverter is the PWM inverter, which can generate a close approximation to the ideal sinusoidal current. Inverters may be further divided into two groups: line-commutated inverters and self-commutated. An AC/DC converter operating in the inverting mode (see section 7.3) is an example of a line-commutated inverter, where the periodic reversal of the AC line voltage impresses a reverse voltage on any conducting thyristor; this allows the thyristor to turn off and transfer its current to another thyristor or diode. In self-commutated inverters, there is no externally impressed alternating line voltage which

193

can be used to commutate a thyristor; the semiconductor switches must be turned off at the correct times by the control circuits.

The majority of inverters for AC motor control are of the self-commutated type. Since thyristors require additional commutation circuitry to turn them off, they are used mainly in high-power inverters. Small inverters, with power ratings up to about 20 kW, generally use power transistors, power MOSFETs or IGBTs. Larger inverters, up to about 100 kW, may use GTOs or thyristors. In power ratings above 100 kW, inverters are almost exclusively based on thyristors.

8.2 Three-phase bridge inverter

The inverter circuits considered in this section are all of the self-commutated type. It is possible to design voltage-source inverters using any of the available semiconductor switching devices; details of the driver and commutation circuits will be found in texts such as Williams [2]. For simplicity, only the main power components will be shown for voltage-source inverter circuits. The power switch will be shown as a power transistor, but this is merely by way of illustration; any other suitable device may be used, together with its associated driver or commutation circuits.

Voltage-source inverter

Figure 8.1 shows the basic circuit of a three-phase bridge inverter operating from a constant-voltage source. Each output line is connected to the mid-point of a pair of power switches; by closing one or other of the power switches, the output line is connected alternately to the positive and negative DC supply lines. It is essential, of course, that both switches are not closed simultaneously, otherwise they would short-circuit the DC supply; the driver circuits must allow sufficient time for one device to switch off before the other is turned on.

Any practical load connected to the AC output lines will possess inductance, which will not permit the current to change instantaneously. When a power switch is turned off, the current must find an alternative path; this is provided by the *feedback diodes* in anti-parallel with the power switches. The operation is as follows. Suppose that initially transistor T_1 is on, connecting line 'a' to the positive DC rail. When T_1 is turned off, the current in line 'a' will transfer to diode D_2, and the potential of line 'a' will fall to that of the negative DC rail. If base drive is applied to transistor T_2, it will turn on when the current in diode D_2 falls to zero; the current in line 'a' will then start to increase in the opposite direction.

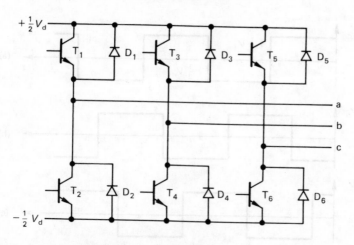

Figure 8.1   Three-phase voltage-source inverter circuit

Six-step inverter

The simplest mode of operation is to control the switches in a sequence which is similar to the natural commutation of the diodes or thyristors in an AC/DC converter (see section 7.3). This results in six switching transistors per cycle of the output AC waveform. Each output line is connected alternately to the positive and negative DC rails; if these are at potentials $+\frac{1}{2}V_d$ and $-\frac{1}{2}V_d$ respectively, then the potential of the output line is a symmetrical square wave as shown in figure 8.2. The line-to-line voltages are the differences between these line potentials, and have the quasi-square waveforms shown in figure 8.2. These waveforms have the same shape as the line current waveforms in figure 7.6 for the AC/DC converter; the line-to-line voltage thus has a substantial harmonic content, with the triplen harmonics eliminated by the three-phase symmetry.

The only way to vary the output voltage of the six-step inverter is to vary the DC supply voltage. This may be done by using either a fully-controlled AC/DC converter, or a rectifier followed by a chopper. The controlled converter has the disadvantage that the input power factor deteriorates as the output voltage is reduced; the rectifier has a high power factor, but this is gained at the cost of the extra chopper stage. Voltage control can be achieved without either of these penalties if the technique of pulse-width modulation (PWM) is applied to the inverter bridge. The principle is similar to that of the DC chopper (section 7.4), where the average output is varied by controlling the duty cycle of a rectangular wave.

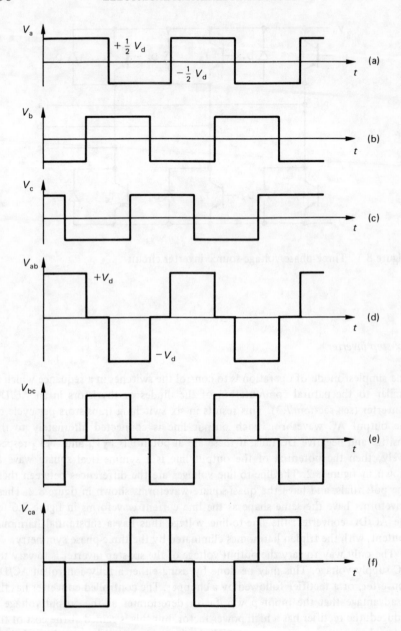

Figure 8.2   Six-step voltage-source inverter waveforms

Sinusoidal PWM inverter

Pulse-width modulation is normally used to shape the output waveform in addition to controlling its amplitude. In the six-step inverter described above, each leg of the bridge is switched twice per cycle, producing a symmetrical square wave at the fundamental output frequency. In a PWM inverter, on the other hand, each leg is switched at a much higher frequency to produce an asymmetrical rectangular wave with a duty cycle which varies periodically. Figure 8.3 shows the potentials of lines 'a', 'b' and 'c', and the resulting line-to-line voltage. When the duty cycle of a line potential is 50 per cent, giving a symmetrical square wave, then the average output is zero; increasing the duty cycle gives a positive average output, and decreasing it gives a negative average output. By controlling the duty cycle, the average value of the rectangular waveform can be made to vary sinusoidally, as shown by the dotted curves in figure 8.3. The amplitude of the sine wave depends on the depth of modulation, which is the deviation of the duty cycle from 50 per cent.

The sinusoidal PWM inverter has two main advantages over the simple six-step inverter. First, the current in an inductive load will be nearly sinusoidal because the inductance has a smoothing effect which attenuates the components of current at the switching frequency. Secondly, the inverter operates with a constant DC link voltage; it can therefore be supplied from a diode bridge rectifier, which draws current from the AC supply at a high power factor.

Murphy and Turnbull [3] give a survey of PWM techniques. The choice of switching frequency is a compromise between the purity of the output current waveform, and switching losses in the inverter. A good sinusoidal current waveform is desirable for AC motor loads (see section 8.5); this implies that the switching frequency should be as high as possible. Power MOSFETs permit a switching frequency of at least 20 kHz, which places any acoustic noise outside the audible frequency range. But MOSFETs are limited in power rating, so high-power PWM inverters must use slower devices operating at reduced switching frequencies.

Current-regulated PWM

Some high-performance AC motor drives require rapid control of the inverter output line current (see section 8.5). This is readily achieved in a PWM inverter by including a current feedback loop in each phase [3]; the current in an AC output line is sensed and used to control the duty cycle of the corresponding leg of the inverter bridge. If the response of the feedback loop is fast enough, it will protect the inverter from faults in the AC load.

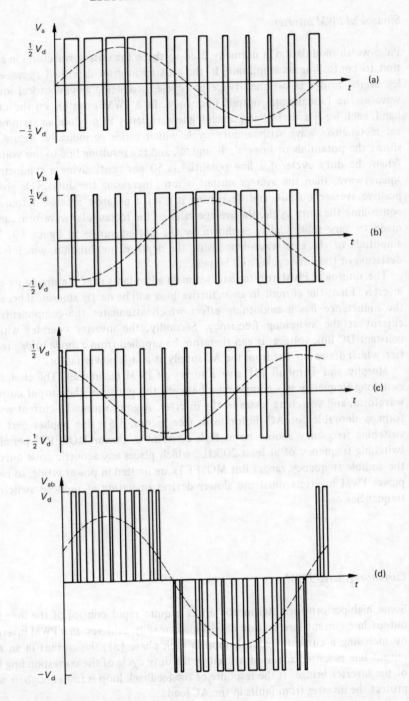

Figure 8.3 Sinusoidal PWM inverter waveforms

Current-source inverter

High-power voltage-source inverters using thyristors require fairly complex commutation circuitry to turn off the conducting devices. If the inverter bridge is supplied from a constant-current source instead of a constant-voltage source, then a much simpler inverter circuit is possible [3]; the most common form is the autosequentially commutated inverter (ASCI). Figure 8.4 shows an inverter of this form. Observe that the diodes are in series with the thyristors, whereas in a voltage-source inverter they are in parallel with the switching devices. In the ASCI circuit the diodes serve to isolate the commutation capacitors from the load. The operation of the circuit is as follows.

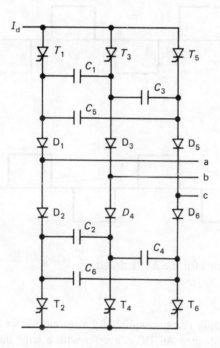

Figure 8.4   Autosequentially commutated inverter (ASCI) circuit

Suppose that thyristors T_1 and T_4 are conducting. Firing T_5 will connect capacitor C_5 across T_1, causing it to turn off and transfer the DC link current I_d to T_5. Similarly, firing T_2 will connect capacitor C_2 across thyristor T_4, causing it to turn off and transfer its current to T_2. Firing continues sequentially, resulting in the AC output line current waveforms shown in figure 8.5. These waveforms are identical to the AC supply current waveforms in a three-phase bridge rectifier with a highly inductive load (figure 7.7).

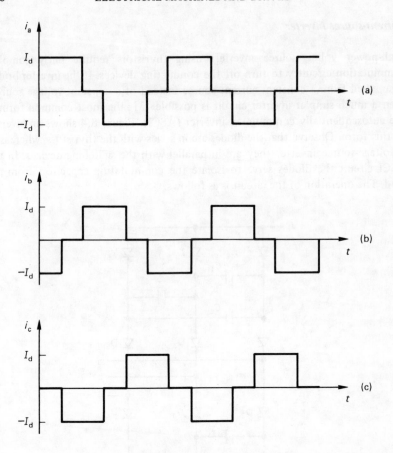

Figure 8.5   Waveforms for the ASCI circuit

The constant supply current required by a current-source inverter can be provided by a fully-controlled AC/DC converter with a large inductance in the DC link between the converter and the inverter. A current feedback loop is used to control the converter firing angle to maintain a constant link current.

Regeneration

A particular advantage of the combination of an AC/DC converter and a current-source inverter is that reverse power flow is handled automatically. If the inverter supplies a machine which attempts to regenerate and feed power into the inverter, then the DC link voltage will reverse. The current feedback loop will increase the firing angle of the AC/DC converter, causing it to operate in the inverting mode and return power to the AC supply. This is in marked contrast to a voltage-source inverter, where the DC link *current* must reverse when the load regenerates. Since an AC/DC converter cannot handle reverse current, an alternative path must be found for the current. This path can take the form of a resistor which is connected across the DC link automatically when the current reverses; but the energy loss limits this solution to powers below about 10 kW. A more efficient solution, which is appropriate for higher powers, is to provide an inverse-parallel converter in the same way as for regenerative DC drives (see section 7.3).

8.3 Synchronous and reluctance motor drives

Since the speed of a synchronous or reluctance motor depends on the frequency of the AC supply, a variable-speed drive system can be formed from one of these motors and one of the self-commutated inverters considered in section 8.2. External control of the inverter frequency will then control the speed of the motor.

If the inverter frequency is itself derived from the motion of the rotor, then the characteristics of the system are quite different; some of the brushless DC machines considered in chapter 10 come into this category, as does the load-commutated inverter system described below.

Adjustable-frequency operation

Voltage-source inverter

With a voltage-source inverter, the voltage applied to the motor terminals is controlled, and the current is determined by the motor operating conditions. If harmonics are neglected, the equations and phasor diagrams developed in chapters 4 and 5 are valid for variable-frequency operation. An important deduction can be made from eqn [4.55] which relates the induced EMF in a winding to the frequency and the magnetic flux density:

$$e_m \propto f B_m \qquad (8.1)$$

If the armature resistance R_a may be neglected, the applied voltage must equal the induced EMF in the winding. To keep the flux density constant, the voltage must be varied in proportion to the frequency; this is termed constant volts per hertz, or constant V/f, operation. The relationship breaks down at low frequencies, where the applied voltage must overcome the voltage drop in R_a as well as the induced EMF. It is normal practice, therefore, to boost the voltage at low frequencies by modifying the constant V/f characteristic. One method is to add an offset to the voltage, equal to the voltage drop in R_a, so that the V–f characteristic is a line which does not pass through the origin; other methods use non-linear V–f characteristics [3].

Phasor diagrams and equations may be used to describe variable-frequency operation; they have the same form as for fixed-frequency operation, but some quantities depend on the frequency in the following way. The magnitude of the excitation voltage E must be proportional to frequency because it represents the EMF induced by rotation of the magnetised rotor. The reactances X_d, X_q and X_s are also proportional to frequency. The torque equation for a three-phase machine with p pairs of poles may be deduced from eqn (5.10), which is valid when the armature resistance R_a may be neglected:

$$T = \frac{3p}{L_d} \left\{ \left(\frac{V}{\omega}\right) \left(\frac{E}{\omega}\right) \sin\delta + \tfrac{1}{2} \left(\frac{V}{\omega}\right) \left(\frac{L_d}{L_q} - 1\right) \sin 2\delta \right\} \tag{8.2}$$

where L_d and L_q are the inductances corresponding to the machine reactances X_d and X_q, and $\omega = 2\pi f$. Since E is proportional to ω, the term E/ω is constant; so if V/ω is held constant, then the maximum torque is constant, and the torque/load-angle characteristic shown in figure 5.20 is valid for adjustable-frequency operation.

The two terms in eqn (8.2) represent synchronous torque and reluctance torque as before. If the machine is non-salient, so that $L_d = L_q$, then the $\sin 2\delta$ reluctance torque term vanishes. If there is no rotor excitation winding, or permanent magnet, then the $\sin\delta$ synchronous torque term vanishes and the machine is a reluctance motor.

Variation of torque with frequency

An inverter is usually designed to deliver a maximum voltage equal to the motor-rated voltage at a specific frequency – the *base frequency* – which will be the normal AC mains frequency for a standard motor. At frequencies below the base frequency, constant V/f control is normally used, which gives constant torque for a given load angle. For operation above the base frequency, however, the voltage cannot be increased; the flux density in the machine will fall, resulting in reduced torque if the load angle is kept constant. The effect on the torque may be deduced from eqn (8.2). In a non-salient machine, the torque will vary as $1/f$, so the mechanical power output – which is proportional to Tf – will remain constant. The output characteristic thus changes from constant torque to constant power when the frequency is increased above the base value. In a reluctance motor, the torque will vary as $1/f^2$ when the voltage is constant; the mechanical power output will therefore vary as $1/f$ at frequencies above the base value.

Current-source inverter

With a current-source inverter the armature current is controlled, and the terminal voltage takes a value demanded by the frequency and the load angle. For a non-salient machine it is convenient to express the torque in terms of the armature current I and a *current load-angle* δ_i; this is equal to the angle δ_{12} between the stator and rotor field components shown in figure 5.2. From figure 5.11 it may be shown that δ_i is given by

$$\delta_i = \delta - \phi + \pi/2 \tag{8.3}$$

where δ is positive for motoring operation and ϕ is positive for a lagging power factor. The torque in terms of δ_i is

$$T = 3p \left(\frac{E}{\omega}\right) I \sin \delta_i \tag{8.4}$$

An immediate deduction from eqn (8.4) is that the minimum current for a given torque occurs when $\delta_i = \pi/2$ radians. This fact is exploited in brushless DC motors (see chapter 9) and in vector control of synchronous motors (see section 8.5). A further consequence is that the current-controlled motor will lose synchronism when δ_i exceeds $\pi/2$ radians, unless there is closed-loop control of the load angle by adjustment of the current.

A current-source inverter will maintain constant current at frequencies below the base value, and the motor terminal voltage will then fall as the frequency is reduced. Unlike the voltage-source inverter, there is no need to allow for armature resistance at low frequencies; the terminal voltage will vary automatically. But at frequencies above the base value the inverter output will become voltage-limited, so it will not be possible to maintain constant current. The operating characteristic will then be similar to that of a drive with a voltage-source inverter.

Load-commutated inverter operation

The EMF generated by a synchronous machine can be used to commutate the inverter, thus eliminating the forced commutation circuitry in a thyristor inverter. An effective synchronous-motor drive system for high power levels – up to several megawatts – can be formed from a fully controlled AC/DC converter supplying a load-commutated inverter, as shown in figure 8.6. Special techniques are required to start the motor [3, 4], because there is no generated EMF when the rotor is stationary. Because the thyristors are naturally commutated, converter grade devices can be used in the inverter; this makes it economical for high power ratings.

The inverter frequency is not externally controlled, but is determined by the speed – and hence the frequency – of the synchronous machine itself. Speed control is achieved by adjusting the DC link voltage, via the firing angle of the supply-side AC/DC converter. The inverter supplying the motor is operated near to its maximum voltage inversion condition, with a large firing angle, so that there is a fixed relationship between DC link voltage and motor terminal voltage. Thus the motor terminal voltage, which is proportional to speed, is forced to follow the DC link voltage. This control scheme is similar to the speed control of a DC motor by adjustment of the armature supply voltage.

Reverse power flow is possible with this system for regenerative braking of the motor, by reversal of the DC link voltage. With appropriate firing angles, the inverter then acts as a phase-controlled converter, supplying power to the DC link; the AC/DC converter operates in the inverting mode, returning power to the AC supply.

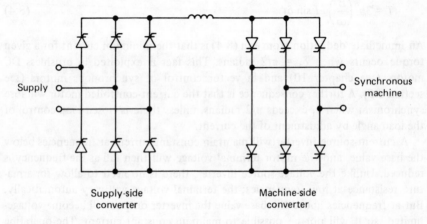

Figure 8.6   Synchronous motor drive with a load-commutated inverter

8.4 Inverter-fed induction motor drives

With synchronous motor drives, there is a distinction between adjustable-frequency operation where the inverter frequency is externally controlled, and self-synchronous operation where the inverter frequency is determined by the speed of the rotor. Induction-motor drives are always of the adjustable-frequency kind, because the rotor magnetic field does not have an independent existence but is caused by currents induced from the stator by transformer action.

This difference between synchronous and induction motors has implications for speed control systems. With a synchronous machine, precise speed control is possible without feedback because the rotor must run in synchronism with the rotating magnetic field. An induction motor, on the other hand, must always run with a speed difference – the slip speed – between the rotor and the rotating magnetic field. The change in slip between no-load and full-load will result in a small speed variation if the inverter frequency is held constant. In many applications this is unimportant; open-loop control with an adjustable-frequency inverter is then a popular and economical choice for a variable-speed drive. If greater speed accuracy is required, comparable with a synchronous-motor drive, then a feedback system must be used to sense the motor speed and adjust the inverter frequency accordingly. Murphy and Turnbull [3] describe several closed-loop control schemes; this section is restricted to open-loop control.

Constant V/f operation

If the stator resistance is negligible then the flux density will be constant if the radio V/f is constant. This may be deduced from the equivalent circuit in figure 6.12 with the resistances R_1 and R_c omitted; the magnetising current I_{0m} will then be constant, provided that the slip s varies inversely with f. As will be seen shortly, this restriction on s implies that the torque is independent of the frequency. At low frequencies the voltage drop in the stator resistance will be significant, which makes it necessary to depart from a constant V/f characteristic, in the same way as with synchronous motors (see section 8.3.).

The torque given by eqn (6.20), which is derived from the approximate equivalent circuit in figure 6.13, may be expressed in the following form:

$$T = \frac{3p}{L}\left(\frac{V_1}{\omega}\right)\frac{1}{\omega_2 L/R_2' + R_2'/\omega_2 L} \tag{8.5}$$

where ω_2 is the rotor, or slip, angular frequency given by

$$\omega_2 = p\omega_s - p\omega_r = \omega - p\omega_r \tag{8.6}$$

If V/f is constant, eqn (8.5) shows that the torque is independent of the supply frequency, but depends on the slip angular frequency ω_2. From eqn (8.6), this frequency is proportional to the difference between the synchronous speed and the rotor speed. The torque/speed characteristics for different supply frequencies thus take the form shown in figure 8.7, where each characteristic has the same shape but is shifted horizontally so that it cuts the zero torque axis at the synchronous speed $\omega_s = \omega/p$. For the normal working torque range, each characteristic is approximately a straight line; the torque/speed characteristic is similar to that of a DC motor with variable-voltage control (section 7.5).

Variable-frequency starting

Figure 8.7 shows that the starting torque will increase as the supply frequency ω is reduced, with a maximum value equal to the breakdown torque. If the frequency is further reduced, the starting torque will fall below the breakdown value. Since the motor operation is now in the favourable region to the right of the breakdown point, the current will be much reduced (see figure 6.16). The starting torque and current will both fall with further reduction in the supply frequency. An initial frequency can be chosen to give the required starting torque, with a corresponding value of current; raising the frequency will accelerate the rotor to its final speed. This method of starting is much less onerous than direct-on-line (DOL) starting at the fixed mains frequency, because the starting current will usually be less than the full-load value. In contrast, the current with DOL starting is typically six times the full-load value.

Since the rotor resistance is no longer constrained by starting requirements, it can be made smaller to give a low slip at normal load. A motor designed for variable-frequency operation can therefore be more efficient than one designed for fixed-frequency operation.

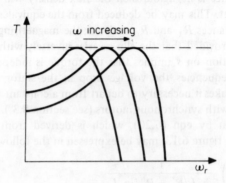

Figure 8.7   Induction-motor torque/speed characteristic for constant V/f

Constant voltage operation

Constant V/f operation is usually restricted to speeds below the base speed by an inverter which is designed to deliver maximum output voltage at the base frequency. As with synchronous motors, the base speed is generally the normal operating speed at the mains frequency with rated voltage. Operation above the base speed is possible, but this entails a reduction in the torque capability. From eqn (8.5), the torque at a given slip frequency will vary as $1/f^2$. To some extent the effect of falling torque can be counteracted by increasing the slip; but the torque must be less than the breakdown value, and this also varies as $1/f^2$, as can be seen by rearranging eqn (6.21):

$$T_m = \frac{3pV_1^2}{2L\omega^2} \tag{8.7}$$

From eqn (8.5) the corresponding slip frequency is given by

$$\omega_2 L/R_s' = 1 \tag{8.8}$$

which shows that the breakdown point occurs at a slip frequency which is independent of the supply frequency.

Above the base speed, there will be a limited range of constant-power operation where the torque varies as $1/f$ by allowing the slip frequency to increase. Once the maximum slip frequency is reached, corresponding to the breakdown point, the power output will vary as $1/f$; this is similar to the behaviour of a reluctance motor (see section 8.3).

8.5 AC drive system performance

Vector control

The DC machine has dominated the variable-speed drive market because the speed and the torque are easily controlled. Armature voltage control provides a simple general-purpose variable-speed drive. Armature current control permits direct control of the torque, which is required for good dynamic response in high-performance closed-loop drives. A similar performance is now possible with AC drives through a technique known as vector control or field-oriented control.

The basic principle of vector control is to use an external controller to reproduce the field relationships which occur naturally in a DC machine. Recall that the field flux and the armature reaction flux in a DC machine are fixed at right angles by the commutator; this has three consequences. First, if magnetic saturation is insignificant, the working flux in the machine is set by the field system independently of the armature current. Secondly, the torque depends only on the product of the armature current and the flux; there is no variable load angle. Thirdly, the machine develops the maximum possible torque for a given armature current and field flux.

Synchronous motors

Figure 5.2 shows the space vectors representing the magnetic flux density components in a synchronous machine. Vector control requires the control of the stator currents so that the angle δ_{12} is held constant at $\pi/2$ radians. There will be a corresponding right-angle relationship between the vectors representing the stator and rotor current densities. This relationship can be achieved by measuring the rotor position with a resolver or a shaft-angle encoder, and using the position to control an inverter supplying currents to the three stator phases. From eqn (8.4) the torque is then:

$$T = 3p \left(\frac{E}{\omega} \right) I \tag{8.9}$$

where I is the stator phase current and E is the EMF induced in one phase by the magnetised rotor. Since the current load-angle is always $\pi/2$ radians, a vector-controlled synchronous motor cannot lose synchronism. From eqn (8.9), if the rotor excitation is held constant, then the torque is directly proportional to current. This relationship also holds under dynamic conditions, provided that the right-angle relationship between the fields is preserved.

Induction motors

Similar principles apply to the vector control of induction motors, although the controller is considerably more complicated. The basic idea may be seen from figure 6.8, which shows the flux-density and current-density distributions in the machine, and from figure 6.9 which shows the corresponding space vectors. In figure 6.9, the total stator current-density vector K_1 has a component K_0 which sets up the flux-density vector B in the machine, and a component K_2' which opposes the rotor induced current-density K_2. Since these current-density components set up corresponding flux-density components, it follows from eqn (4.33) that the torque is proportional to $K_0 K_2'$. Note that the space-vector diagram is valid for transient conditions as well as steady-state, because it merely represents the sinusoidal spatial distribution of quantities at a particular instant of time.

The principle of vector control is to define independently the flux-producing component of current-density K_0 and the torque-producing component K_2'. This allows independent control of the flux and the torque, as in a DC machine. To implement vector control, it is necessary to determine the direction of the flux-density vector B; then the desired current-density components K_0 and K_2' define a stator current-density vector K_1 which is created by currents in the three stator phases. The system requires instantaneous control of the phase currents, which can be achieved with a current-regulated PWM inverter or a current-source inverter.

A problem in implementing vector control of induction motors is to determine the position of the flux-density vector. Direct measurement with field sensors in the machine is possible, but of limited practical value. The preferred method is to infer the position of the flux-density vector from measurements of the stator terminal voltage and current and the rotor speed. This requires a mathematical model of the machine which is valid under dynamic conditions; see Murphy and Turnbull [3] for a brief account, and Leonhard [5] for a comprehensive treatment.

Vector control offers no particular advantage when the motor load torque is steady or varies only slowly. Its chief merit is a good dynamic response to rapidly changing loads. The vector-controlled induction motor then combines the control characteristics of the DC motor with the merits of the induction motor: the motor is smaller, cheaper and more robust than its DC counterpart; it requires little maintenance, and it is well suited to hazardous or hostile environments.

Drive stability

Speed instability can occur in variable-speed drives which use AC motors supplied from adjustable-frequency inverters; the instability generally occurs at frequencies well below the normal mains frequency. Reluctance motors are particularly prone to this kind of instability, typically in the frequency range 5–20 Hz, where the speed oscillates above and below the synchronous speed. Induction motors are more stable, but they may also exhibit this effect.

Murphy and Turnbull [3] identify two sources of speed instability: inherent instability in the motor, and instability due to interaction between the motor and the inverter. Most designs of reluctance motor are inherently unstable under some conditions of frequency, voltage and load. Synchronous and induction motors are usually stable when the AC supply impedance is very low, but may become unstable when supplied from inverters with an appreciable output impedance. The instability can take the form of an interchange of energy between the motor inertia and the filter components in the DC link of the inverter.

Both kinds of instability can often be cured by a closed-loop control system. Vector control appears to offer improved stability as a benefit additional to its good dynamic performance.

Effects of nonsinusoidal supply waveforms

In normal mains operation, the stator currents in a three-phase AC machine are approximately sinusoidal; consequently the stator magnetic field rotates at an almost constant speed, and it exerts a steady torque on the rotor. When the machine is supplied from an inverter, the currents may be markedly non-sinusoidal; an extreme case is the six-step current-source inverter (see section 8.3), where the currents are quasi-square waves. With this waveform, the currents remain static for a sixth of a cycle at a time, and then change abruptly. The magnetic field therefore rotates in a series of jerks, and exerts a corresponding pulsating torque on the rotor. This is the most severe case, but any departure from a purely sinusoidal current will result in a pulsating component of torque. One of the advantages of PWM inverters is that they give current waveforms which are more nearly sinusoidal.

The behaviour of a motor supplied from a nonsinusoidal voltage or current source may be determined by Fourier analysis [3]; the applied waveform is represented by a fundamental component and a series of harmonics, and the motor performance for each component is determined. The total current or mean torque is then the sum of the individual terms, provided that (a) magnetic non-linearity can be neglected, and (b) the rotor speed can be regarded as constant. Each harmonic component will generate a rotating magnetic field; it may be shown that the speeds and directions of these component fields, relative to the fundamental, are as follows for the first 13 harmonics:

Harmonic number	Speed	Direction
1	ω_s	+
5	$5\omega_s$	−
7	$7\omega_s$	+
11	$11\omega_s$	−
13	$13\omega_s$	+

The triplen harmonics are missing because of the three-phase symmetry; and the fields of the 5th and 11th harmonics rotate backwards.

Mean torque

With induction motors, the harmonic components of current can contribute to the mean torque because they induce corresponding currents in the rotor; but the slip will be high for these components because the speed of the field is much greater than the speed of the rotor. In a typical motor the harmonic torques will be small, and they will tend to cancel out in pairs because the forward and backward field components give torques in opposite directions. The net effect is negligible.

In synchronous and reluctance motors, the harmonics do not rotate in synchronism with the rotor, so they cannot develop a steady component of synchronous or reluctance torque.

Pulsating torque

Component fields with different harmonic numbers can interact to produce pulsating components of torque. Relative to the fundamental field, the 5th harmonic field rotates at a speed of $-6\omega_s$, and the 7th harmonic field rotates at a speed of $+6\omega_s$. Both of these fields will interact with the fundamental to produce a torque pulsation at 6 times the fundamental frequency. Similarly, the 11th and 13th harmonics will produce a torque pulsation at 12 times the fundamental frequency, and so on for higher harmonics. These components will occur in all AC machines, and they can be troublesome at low speeds. The rotor inertia will have an increasing smoothing effect as the speed rises, so that less pulsating torque will be transmitted to the load.

Losses

We have seen that the mean torque of an AC motor is almost entirely determined by the fundamental component of current; for a given torque, therefore, the harmonic components of current will give rise to additional losses. These losses will occur in the resistance of the stator winding of any AC motor, and in the rotor winding or cage of an induction motor. The additional rotor loss is magnified by the increase in resistance caused by skin effect [3], so this loss is usually dominant. In addition, the harmonic components of flux density can cause increased losses in the iron core of the machine.

With a six-step voltage-source inverter, the harmonics can increase the total losses of an induction motor by over 20 per cent at full load [3]. This does not make very much difference to the efficiency, but it represents a significant increase in the heat dissipated; some derating of the motor, by reduction of the output torque, may be necessary to avoid overheating.

A PWM inverter with a high switching frequency will give currents with a much lower harmonic content than a six-step inverter; the additional losses are correspondingly lower, so derating is not usually necessary.

Problems

8.1. Derive eqn (8.4) for the torque of a synchronous motor in terms of the current load angle.

8.2. A form of the induction motor equivalent circuit (figure 6.12) may be used for each harmonic component of a non-sinusoidal supply voltage waveform. Show that the reactances in this equivalent circuit must be n times the reactance at the fundamental frequency, where n is the order of the harmonic. Show also that the slip for the harmonic component is $1 \pm (1 - s)/n$, where s is the fundamental slip, and the sign is $-$ for a forward-rotating harmonic field or $+$ for a backward-rotating field.

8.3. For harmonics other than the fundamental, show that the equivalent circuit of problem 8.2 may be approximated by a single reactance of magnitude $n(x_1 + x_2)$, where x_1 and x_2 are the primary and secondary leakage reactances at the fundamental frequency, and n is the order of the harmonic.

8.4. The equivalent circuit of one phase of an induction motor has the following parameter values: $R_1 = 4\ \Omega; x_1 = 4\ \Omega; R_2 = 5\ \Omega; x_2 = 4\ \Omega; X_m = 50\ \Omega$; the core-loss resistance may be neglected. The motor is supplied from a six-step voltage source inverter with a fundamental voltage of 240 V per phase; it operates with a full-load slip of 0.05 at the base frequency. Calculate the contributions of the fundamental, 5th and 7th harmonics to the motor $I^2 R$ loss, assuming that the rotor resistance is independent of frequency.

References

1   C. W. Lander, *Power Electronics*, 2nd ed. (London: McGraw-Hill, 1987).
2   B. W. Williams, *Power Electronics: Devices, Drivers and Applications* (London: Macmillan, 1987).

3 J. M. D. Murphy and F. G. Turnbull, *Power Electronic Control of AC Motors* (Oxford: Pergamon Press, 1988).
4 D. Finney, *Variable Frequency AC Motor Drive Systems* (London: Peter Peregrinus, 1988).
5 W. Leonhard, *Control of Electrical Drives* (Berlin: Springer, 1985).

9   *Stepper Motor Drives*

9.1 Introduction

The conventional synchronous motors considered in chapters 5 and 8 have two distinctive features: the AC armature winding is effectively sinusoidally distributed, and the AC supply is taken from a three-phase source of constant or adjustable frequency. In consequence a synchronous motor develops a smooth torque and it runs at a speed determined by the supply frequency.

Stepper motors, or stepping motors, are related to synchronous motors in the sense that the motion of the rotor is determined by the frequency of currents in the armature windings, but they differ in two important respects. First, the armature windings are not even approximately sinusoidally distributed; secondly, the supply is not sinusoidal AC but switched DC. As its name implies, the function of a stepper motor is to move the rotor through a precise angular step when the current in one or more of the stator windings is switched. The rotor may be driven at a high speed by switching the currents rapidly; but it is still the rotor angular position rather than its velocity which is the controlled quantity.

In a stepper motor the windings are supplied from a controller that switches the currents sequentially in response to successive input drive pulses. Each pulse input to the controller causes an abrupt change in the motor winding currents, which moves the rotor through one step. If pulses are applied at a low repetition rate, the winding currents will remain constant between the pulses and the rotor will come to rest after each step. At high stepping rates the rotor will move continuously, though its velocity will not be constant, and the motor will behave like a conventional synchronous motor.

The correspondence between rotor steps and input pulses makes the stepper motor an ideal device for digital control. Applications include quartz analogue clocks and watches, printers and graph plotters, head positioning in computer disc drives, and numerically controlled machine tools [1, 2]. Stepper motors are made in sizes ranging from milliwatts to tens of kilowatts, and they are expected to replace conventional AC and DC machines in many control applications.

There are three main types of stepper motor: simple permanent-magnet, variable-reluctance, and hybrid. The simple permanent-magnet stepper motor is similar to an ordinary synchronous motor with a permanent-magnet rotor. It differs in the structure of the stator winding, which takes the form of coils wound on salient poles. Energising the windings on one pair of poles will pull the rotor into alignment with those poles; energising the next pair will move the rotor through one step. The torque per unit volume is relatively poor with this type of motor, and the step angle is large: $90°$ in the case of a two-pole rotor. In most applications larger torques and smaller step angles are required, so simple permanent-magnet stepper motors are not widely used; they will not be considered further in this book.

9.2 Variable-reluctance stepper motors

The variable-reluctance stepper motor makes use of the alignment torque principle illustrated in figure 1.17. In this diagram, the iron rotor experiences a torque which tends to rotate it into alignment with the stator poles; the reluctance of the magnetic circuit is a minimum in this position. Most variable-reluctance stepper motors have a more complicated structure than this, but they all utilise the alignment torque between salient poles or teeth on both the stator and the rotor. Variable-reluctance stepper motors are examples of *doubly-salient* machines, whose action cannot be described in terms of the rotating-field concepts used in chapters 4 and 5. They have much in common with the *switched reluctance motors* discussed in section 10.4.

Figure 9.1 shows a cross-section through a simple variable-reluctance motor. There are three stator phases, arranged on six poles, and four rotor poles. The diagram shows three successive positions of the rotor when phases 'a', 'b' and 'c' are energised in sequence; the step angle is $30°$. Notice that the rotor steps are smaller than the successive positions of the magnetic field axis; this is a *vernier* motor. Smaller step angles can be achieved by using more stator and rotor poles, or by employing a multi-stack construction.

In the multi-stack motor [1, 2] there is a separate stator and rotor combination for each phase. The rotor has small salient poles or teeth, and the stator usually has four poles with similar teeth formed in the pole faces. When one phase is energised, all the rotor teeth in that stack are pulled into alignment with the stator teeth. The rotors are mounted on a common shaft, and the stators in successive stacks are displaced by an angle equal to the step angle. Switching the current from one phase to the next will pull the next set of rotor teeth into alignment with the corresponding stator teeth, causing the shaft to rotate through one step. Multi-stack motors usually have at least three phases.

Variable-reluctance stepper motors have the useful property that the torque depends on the magnitude of the current and not its direction; the magnetic alignment force is not affected by a reversal of the field direction. Consequently the current in a phase only needs to be switched on and off; it does not need to be reversed. This greatly simplifies the electronic control of variable-reluctance motors.

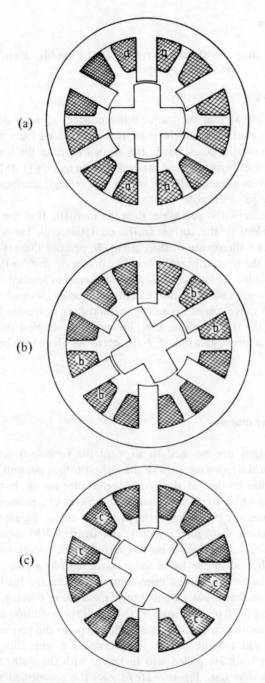

Figure 9.1 Single-stack variable-reluctance stepper motor: (a) phase 'a' energised; (b) phase 'b' energised; (c) phase 'c' energised

Torque production

Equation [1.45] gives the alignment torque in the doubly-salient structure of figure 1.17:

$$T = adgB^2/\mu_0 \text{ newton metres} \qquad\qquad [1.45]$$

which apparently shows that the torque is independent of the angle of rotation. This is approximately true when the rotor is well displaced from its position of alignment with the stator poles; but in the aligned position the torque must be zero. The torque rises from zero to a maximum given by eqn [1.45] as the rotor moves away from its aligned position, with a torque/angle characteristic which depends on the shape of the poles.

If magnetic saturation is negligible, then the magnetic flux density B in the airgap is proportional to the current in the excitation coil. The torque should therefore depend on the square of the current. In practice there is often significant saturation of the iron paths at the normal working current, so the square-law relationship only holds for low currents. At normal current levels the relationship between torque, angle and excitation current is complex; it can be determined numerically by an extension of the energy method given in section 1.4 for linear systems [3]. For the stepper-motor user, however, the simplest procedure is to consult the manufacturer's data sheet for characteristics which have been measured experimentally.

9.3 Hybrid stepper motors

A permanent magnet can be used to augment the variable-reluctance effect, resulting in a hybrid stepper motor with the highest torque per unit volume [1]. The stator is similar to that of the variable-reluctance motor, but the rotor is made in two parts which form the N and S pole-pieces of a permanent magnet. Figure 9.2 illustrates the principles of the two-phase motor. Figure 9.2(a) shows a longitudinal section through the motor, and figure 9.2(b) shows transverse sections through the rotor N and S poles. Unlike the multi-stack variable-reluctance motor, the hybrid motor has a single stator with long poles bridging the two rotor parts; there is an angular displacement between the teeth on the two rotor parts. Coils on stator poles 1 and 3 form the α phase winding, and coils on poles 2 and 4 form the β phase. Figure 9.2(b) shows the condition when phase α is energised with positive current. The stator flux opposes the permanent-magnet flux in gaps 3-N and 1-S, but it aids the permanent-magnet flux in gaps 1-N and 3-S; the rotor teeth are pulled into alignment with the stator teeth in gaps where the field is strongest. Figure 9.2(c) shows the corresponding condition when phase β is energised, so that the teeth are aligned in gaps 2-N and 4-S.

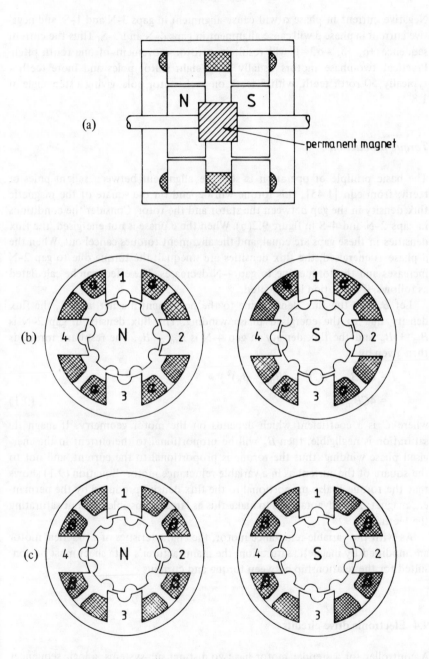

Figure 9.2 Hybrid stepper motor: (a) longitudinal section; (b) transverse section through rotor poles – phase α energised; (c) phase β energised

Negative current in phase α will cause alignment in gaps 3-N and 1-S, and negative current in phase β will cause alignment in gaps 4-N and 2-S. Thus the current sequence $+\alpha$, $+\beta$, $-\alpha$, $-\beta$ will result in a rotor movement of one tooth pitch. Practical two-phase motors usually have eight stator poles and more teeth - typically 50 rotor teeth, with 5 teeth on each stator pole, giving a step angle of $1.8°$.

Torque production

The basic priniple of operation is still the alignment between salient poles or teeth; from eqn [1.45], this torque will depend on the square of the magnetic flux density in the gap between the stator and the rotor. Consider the conditions in gaps 2-N and 4-S in figure 9.2(b). When the β phase is not energised, the flux densities in these gaps are equal, and the alignment torques cancel out. When the β phase is energised, the flux densities are unequal; the torque due to gap 2-N increases and the torque due to gap 4-N decreases. The effect can be calculated as follows, if saturation is neglected.

Let B_m be the flux density due to the permanent magnet, and B_e the flux density due to the energised phase winding. The flux density in gap 2-N is $B_m + B_e$ and the flux density in gap 4-N is $B_m - B_e$. The resultant torque is then given by

$$T = C\{(B_m + B_e)^2 - (B_m - B_e)^2\}$$

$$= 4CB_m B_e \tag{9.1}$$

where C is a coefficient which depends on the motor geometry. If magnetic saturation is negligible, then B_e will be proportional to the current in the energised phase winding; thus the torque is proportional to the current, and not to the square of the current as in a variable-reluctance motor. Equation (9.1) shows that the torque is also proportional to the flux density produced by the permanent magnet; it is advantageous to make this as large as possible without saturating the teeth.

As with the variable-reluctance motor, the characteristics of a practical motor are modified by magnetic saturation; the manufacturer's data sheet must be consulted for the relationship between torque and current.

9.4 Electronic drive circuits

A controller for a stepper motor has two distinct sub-systems: a logic sequencer which generates the required switching signals for the motor windings, and drive circuits which control the winding currents in response to the switching signals.

Drive circuits are broadly classified as unipolar or bipolar. Unipolar drives supply current in one direction only; bipolar drives can reverse the direction of current.

Variable-reluctance stepper motors are well suited to unipolar drives, because the current in a phase only needs to be switched on and off. Motors incorporating permanent magnets, on the other hand, require the field in each phase to be reversed from time to time. This can be achieved by reversing the current in a single winding with a bipolar drive. Alternatively the motor can be provided with *bifilar windings* supplied from unipolar drives; there are two coils on each pole, connected in opposite senses, which permit reversal of the field by switching the current from one coil to the other. The use of bifilar windings simplifies the drive electronics, but there is a performance penalty: only half the space is available for each active winding, so the effective resistance per phase is doubled.

Unipolar drive circuits

Figure 9.3 shows a typical unipolar drive circuit for one motor phase, with the transistor base drive components omitted. The transistor is operated in a switching mode, so that it is either saturated or cut off. When the transistor conducts, current passes through the motor winding; when it ceases to conduct, the winding current is diverted to the freewheeling diode.

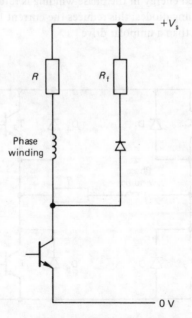

Figure 9.3   Unipolar drive circuit for one motor phase

If the resistors R and R_f were omitted, the time constant L_p/R_p of the phase winding would limit the rate of rise of the current when the transistor turns on and the rate of fall when it turns off; this would limit the speed of operation of the motor. The speed of response is improved by voltage forcing; a high supply voltage is used, and the current is limited by connecting a forcing resistance R in series with the winding as shown in figure 9.3. The time constant is now $L_p/(R_p + R)$, so the current rise-time will be shortened significantly if R is larger than R_p. Although simple, this system is inefficient because of the energy lost in the forcing resistance. The current fall time is further reduced by connecting the resistor R_f in series with the freewheeling diode.

Bipolar drive circuits

Figure 9.4 shows a basic bipolar drive circuit, using four transistors in a bridge configuration; base drive components have again been omitted. Current is passed through the phase winding in one direction by turning on T_1 and T_4, and in the other direction by turning on T_3 and T_2. This circuit uses four times as many power components as the unipolar circuit of figure 9.3, and the base drive circuits are more complex. As with the unipolar drive, voltage forcing with the series resistor R is used to increase the rate of rise of current. When the transistors turn off, some of the stored energy in the phase winding is returned to the DC supply through the freewheeling diodes; this reduces the current fall time and makes the circuit more efficient than a unipolar drive.

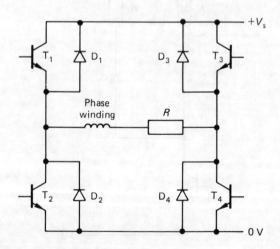

Figure 9.4   Bipolar drive circuit for one motor phase

Chopper drive circuits

With the simple unipolar and bipolar drive circuits, efficiency is sacrificed when voltage forcing is used to reduce the current rise time. A better system is the PWM or chopper drive [1, 2], which gives the benefits of forcing without the energy loss. Figure 9.5 shows the power circuit for one phase of a unipolar chopper drive. To energise the phase winding, transistors T_1 and T_2 are both turned on, connecting the high supply voltage across the winding. R_c is a current-sensing resistor dropping a small voltage which is used to control T_1; when the current rises above its rated value, T_1 is turned off; when the current falls below its rated value, T_1 is turned on again and the cycle repeated. At the end of the excitation period both T_1 and T_2 are turned off; stored energy is then returned to the supply through the freewheeling diodes D_1 and D_2 as in the bipolar drive.

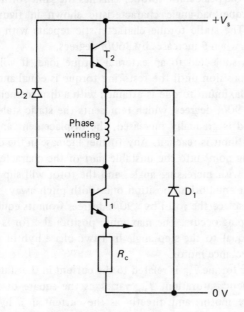

Figure 9.5   Chopper drive circuit for one motor phase

Although it uses more components, the chopper drive is now the preferred system where high performance and good efficiency are required. It does, however, have the disadvantage of acoustic noise from the motor and possible electromagnetic interference from the high-frequency components of voltage and current.

9.5 Stepper motor characteristics

Static torque characteristics

When constant current is passed through one or more phases of a stepper motor, the rotor will experience a torque when it is displaced from its equilibrium step position. This torque tends to restore the rotor to its equilibrium position: a positive displacement will give a negative torque, and vice versa. To a first approximation, the torque of a variable-reluctance or hybrid stepping motor is given by [1]

$$T = -T_m \sin n\theta \qquad (9.2)$$

where θ is the angular displacement of the rotor, n is the number of teeth on the rotor, and T_m is the peak static torque. This has the same form as the synchronous machine torque/load-angle characteristic shown in figure 5.10, with δ replaced by $n\theta$. The static torque characteristic repeats with a period of one rotor tooth pitch, when θ increases by $360/n$ degrees.

If the rotor is subjected to an external torque load, it will move from its equilibrium step position until the restoring torque is equal and opposite to the applied torque. Maximum torque is attained with a displacement of a quarter of a tooth pitch, or $90/n$ degrees, which represents the static stability limit. If the static torque load is gradually increased, the displacement angle will increase until the stability limit is reached. Any further increase in the displacement will take the operating point into the unstable part of the characteristic, where the torque decreases with increasing angle, and the rotor will slip a tooth – it will move to the next equilibrium position one tooth pitch away. It follows that a static load can displace the rotor by $\pm 90/n$ degrees from its equilibrium position before tooth slipping occurs. The maximum positional error is therefore $\pm 90/n$ degrees; this is equal to the step angle in a two-phase hybrid motor or a four-stack variable-reluctance motor.

The peak static torque T_m is related to the current in the stator phases. In the absence of magnetic saturation, T_m varies as the square of the current in a variable-reluctance motor, and directly as the current in a hybrid motor (see sections 9.2 and 9.3). In practice there is usually considerable saturation, and the variation of torque with current must be obtained from manufacturers' data.

Multi-step operation

If a single pulse is applied to a stepper motor drive unit, the phase currents will switch to the next step position and the rotor will move to a new equilibrium position. The torque/displacement characteristic is a spring-like characteristic, where the restoring torque increases with displacement; consequently the rotor will oscillate about its new equilibrium position. When repetitive pulses are applied at a low rate, the rotor will move in steps but it will oscillate about each step position. If the next drive pulse is applied before the oscillation has decayed to a low level, then resonance can occur, and the oscillation amplitude may grow until the motor operation becomes erratic [1]. Resonance can occur at stepping rates such that the time between drive pulses is a multiple of the rotor oscillation period; the critical stepping rates are thus given by

$$f_r = f_n/k, \quad k = 1, 2, 3, \ldots \qquad (9.3)$$

where f_r is the resonant stepping rate and f_n is the rotor natural frequency of oscillation. Acarnley [1] discusses mechanical and electromagnetic methods of damping the rotor oscillation; Kenjo and Nagamori [2] describe some electronic methods of controlling the oscillation by adjusting the pulse timing when only a few steps are required.

High-speed operation

When the stepping rate is higher than the rotor natural frequency, the motion of the rotor is continuous and the small speed variations between steps can be ignored. This mode of operation is known as 'slewing', which resembles the normal operation of a conventional synchronous motor.

Start/stop rate

Provided that the stepping rate is not too high, a stepper motor will start and run synchronously in the slewing mode when a train of drive pulses is suddenly applied; it will also stop suddenly when the pulse train stops. There is a critical stepping rate known as the start/stop rate; below this rate a stepper motor will start and stop with the pulse train, and the number of rotor steps will equal the number of drive pulses; above this rate the rotor may fail to accelerate, or it may run on for several steps when the pulse train stops. The start/stop rate depends on the total rotor inertia as well as the properties of the motor and the drive unit.

Pull-out torque

As with a synchronous motor, a slewing stepper motor will stall when the applied torque exceeds a value known as the pull-out torque. The pull-out torque varies with stepping rate; an explanation is as follows. Figure 9.6 shows the measured pull-out torque characteristic for a typical small hybrid stepper motor supplied from a chopper drive unit. At low stepping rates the drive unit forces the currents in the motor phases to be almost rectangular pulses of constant amplitude, and the pull-out torque is nearly constant. Since the phases are inductive, it takes time for the current to rise to its full value; this time will form a larger proportion of the step time at higher stepping rates, so the mean current will fall and the pull-out torque will decrease. At still higher stepping rates the step time will be too short for the current to reach its full value, and the mean current will be further reduced.

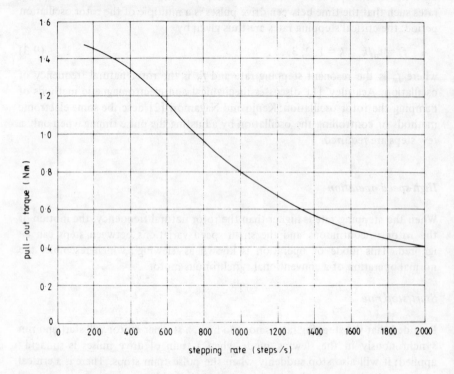

Figure 9.6   Pull-out torque characteristic for a hybrid stepper motor

9.6 Stepper-motor control

Open-loop control

One of the most useful features of the stepper motor is that the speed or position of the rotor can be accurately controlled without feedback. For speed control, it is merely necessary to ensure that the rotor does not lose synchronism with the drive pulses. Position control imposes the further restriction that the rotor must not skip any steps when accelerating or decelerating. These conditions are satisfied automatically if the motor is operated below its start/stop rate; but this is unduly restricting, since the motor is capable of running at much higher speeds.

Velocity profile

If a stepper motor is to be run at a speed above the start/stop rate, then it must be started at a lower speed and accelerated by increasing the stepping rate progressively. The converse is required to stop the motor in a controlled manner. A graph of stepping rate against time is termed a velocity profile; figure 9.7 shows a typical profile for starting and stopping a motor. The velocity profile is non-linear because there is less accelerating torque available at high stepping rates. This follows from the fact that the maximum torque available for acceleration or deceleration is somewhat less than the pull-out torque, and figure 9.6 shows that this torque falls with increasing stepping rate. If the available torque falls linearly with increasing stepping rate, then the required shape for the velocity profile is exponential. Since a straight line is often a good approximation to the torque characteristic, an exponential velocity profile is widely used.

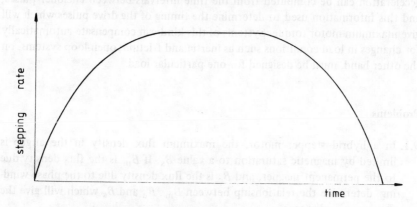

Figure 9.7 Velocity profile for acceleration and deceleration

Speed and position control

By varying the stepping rate in accordance with a calculated velocity profile, it is possible to use the full speed range of the motor. In speed-control systems this allows the motor to run at a high speed; in position-control systems it permits rapid movement to the final position when the rotor is required to turn through a large angle. Open-loop control of this kind is easily implemented with microprocessors [1, 2]. It should be noted, however, that the velocity profile cannot be determined directly from the static pull-out torque characteristic because the motor may fail to develop the full static torque under dynamic conditions. In practice it is often sufficient to apply a derating factor to the static torque, and then calculate the shape of the velocity profile from a straight-line approximation to the pull-out torque curve. Derating factors are usually determined experimentally; typical values are 0.8 for speed control and 0.5 for position control.

Closed-loop control

Open-loop control using a velocity profile is simple and economical, but fails to exploit the full torque capability of the motor. We have already seen that a torque value well below the static pull-out value must be used in calculating the profile; there will also need to be a factor of safety to allow for variations in the load conditions. Better performance is possible with closed-loop control systems [1, 2] which sense the rotor position.

Usually the rotor position is sensed digitally with an incremental encoder which generates one pulse for each rotor position step. The rotor velocity and acceleration can be computed from the time intervals between encloder pulses, and this information used to determine the timing of the drive pulses which will give maximum motor torque. Systems of this kind can compensate automatically for changes in load conditions such as inertia and friction; open-loop systems, on the other hand, must be designed for one particular load.

Problems

9.1. In a hybrid stepper motor, the maximum flux density in the airgap is limited by magnetic saturation to a value B_s. If B_m is the flux density due to the permanent magnet, and B_e is the flux density due to the phase winding, determine the relationship between B_m, B_e and B_s which will give the maximum motor torque.

9.2. A stepper motor has a pullout-torque/stepping-rate characteristic which falls linearly from an initial torque T_i at a stepping rate S_i, to a final torque T_f at a stepping rate S_f. If the rotating system has a polar moment of inertia J and the load torque may be treated as a constant T_L, show that the theoretical velocity profile is given by $S = a - b \exp(-kt)$ for $S_i < S < S_f$, and determine the values of a, b and k.

References

1 P. P. Acarnley, *Stepping Motors: a Guide to Modern Theory and Practice*, 2nd ed. (London: Peter Peregrinus, 1984).

2 T. Kenjo, *Stepping Motors and their Microprocessor Controls* (Oxford University Press, 1984).

3 J. M. Stephenson and J. Corda, 'Computation of torque and current in doubly salient reluctance motors from nonlinear magnetisation data', *Proc. IEE*, **126** (1979), pp. 393-6.

10 Brushless and Switched Reluctance Drives

10.1 Introduction

The machines covered in this chapter may be classified as electronically commutated motors. Brushless DC motors are related to classical DC and AC motors; switched reluctance motors are related to stepper motors. They all feature electronic switching of the stator currents, controlled by the position of the rotor, to give continuous motion. It is this use of a rotor position sensor which makes these drives fundamentally different from the AC and DC drives of chapters 7 and 8, and leads to a close connection between the design of the motor and the design of the power electronic controller.

Brushless DC motors

In the classical DC motor, the brushes and commutator act as a set of mechanical switches controlling the currents in the armature conductors. If these are replaced with semiconductor switches, the result is a brushless DC (BLDC) motor. Since it is simpler to have the switches stationary, the functions of stator and rotor are interchanged; the rotor carries a permanent-magnet field system, and the armature coils are on the stator. Semiconductor switches – usually transistors – must reverse the currents in the armature coils at the correct instants as the field poles rotate; it is thus necessary to sense the rotor position and use this to control the switches.

The BLDC motor is a form of synchronous machine, since the stator coils carry alternating currents which produce a magnetic field rotating in synchronism with the rotor. It differs from the conventional synchronous machine of chapter 5 in two ways: the axis between the stator and the rotor magnetic fields is fixed at $90°$, and the frequency is not defined externally but is determined by the rotor speed. A BLDC motor thus resembles the vector-controlled synchronous motor described in section 8.5.

BLDC motors have essentially the same terminal characteristics as classical DC motors. Although they are more expensive, they generally offer more output from a given frame size, with a higher efficiency [1]. The elimination of brushes makes for high reliability and low maintenance; and the absence of sparking makes them suitable for hazardous environments. Permanent-magnet BLDC motors are normally limited to power levels below about 20 kW for the same reasons as classical DC motors: see section 2.5.

There are two basic types of BLDC motor: squarewave and sinewave. The squarewave type is derived from the classical DC motor, and has a square current waveform; the sinewave type is derived from the classical synchronous motor, and has a sinusoidal current waveform. There are corresponding differences in the internal design of the motor. Squarewave motors have a higher output for a given frame size, and use simpler power electronic controllers; sinewave motors give a smoother torque, and are more easily designed in large sizes.

Switched reluctance motors

A switched reluctance (SR) motor is similar in structure to a variable-reluctance stepper motor, but its function is quite different. Whereas the stepper motor is designed to move the rotor through defined angles in response to external drive pulses, the SR motor is designed for continuous rotation at high speeds. This difference is reflected in the electronic controllers; like the BLDC motor, the SR motor uses rotor position sensing to switch the currents in the stator winding.

SR motors can offer performance advantages over classical AC motors for variable-speed drives. The controller is simpler than a conventional inverter; an SR motor can give a higher output than an induction motor of the same size; and the overall drive system efficiency can be higher than for an inverter-fed induction motor [2]. Disadvantages of SR drives include torque pulsation at low speeds, and noise. These unwanted effects are smaller in the latest designs, but they cannot be eliminated altogether.

A notable feature of the SR drive is the intimate connection between the design of the motor and the design of the electronic controller. Torque pulsation at low speeds, for example, is affected by the motor design; it is also affected by the controller current waveform, which in turn is influenced by the motor design.

10.2 Squarewave brushless DC drives

In a classical DC motor, the field flux density is nearly constant under the poles; a graph of flux-density against angle is almost a square wave (figure 2.8). Likewise the current in an individual armature conductor remains constant until it is reversed by the commutator, so a graph of current against time is almost a square wave.

We have seen that the classical DC motor develops an almost constant torque and generated EMF as a result of the interaction of the squarewave currents with a squarewave flux density. It is natural to attempt to reproduce these conditions in a brushless DC (BLDC) motor. There is one important difference, however, between a classical DC motor and its brushless counterpart. In a classical motor, the number of commutator segments can be very large. It would be uneconomic to duplicate this in the brushless motor with a large number of semiconductor switches and a corresponding number of motor phases. BLDC motors usually employ just three phases, supplied by a three-phase bridge circuit similar to the inverters described in section 8.2. The design of a BLDC motor therefore requires some care if it is to emulate the performance of its classical counterpart. There is a significant difference between motors with star-connected windings and those with delta-connected windings.

The switching of the inverter phases must be synchronised with the rotor position. This may be accomplished with optical sensors and a slotted disc which allows light to fall on a sensor when the rotor is in the correct position for phase switching. A popular alternative to the optical method uses Hall-effect sensors activated by magnets on the rotor; these may be extensions of the main rotor magnets, or they may be auxiliary magnets.

Star-connected motor

Figure 10.1(a) shows a simplified representation of the structure of a two-pole BLDC motor designed for star connection of the three stator phases; constructional details will be found in references [1] and [3]. The stator carries a three-phase distributed winding in slots, similar to that of a classical AC machine, except that there is no overlap between the phase groups (see section 4.8). In figure 10.1(a) the individual slots and conductors are not shown; the segments labelled 'a' and 'a̅', for example, would contain several slots in a practical machine.

The rotor in figure 10.1(a) shows the principle used in many small BLDC motors: permanent magnets are mounted directly on the surface of a steel cylinder. These magnets may be of ferrite or a rare-earth alloy (usually NdFeB – see section 1.7). The magnets each span $180°$ and they have opposite polarities; they are magnetised radially, so that all the conductors under one magnet will experience virtually the same value of flux density.

Current is supplied to the star-connected stator winding from a controller using a three-phase bridge circuit of the same form as the inverter shown in figure 8.1. Control of the bridge is slightly different from that of a normal voltage-source inverter, however. In the inverter there are always three semiconductor switches closed at any instant of time: one in each phase of the bridge. But in the controller for a BLDC motor, only two switches are closed at any instant; both of the switches in the third phase are open, allowing the current in the corresponding output line to decay to zero through the feedback diodes.

Figure 10.1(b) shows the connection of the stator phases. For the rotor position shown in figure 10.1(a), current flows from line 1 to line 2, giving $i_b = -i_a$ and $i_c = 0$. This current pattern is maintained for $60°$ of rotation of the rotor. During this interval the currents in phase bands 'a' and 'b' under a rotor N pole are in the positive direction; the currents in phase bands 'a̅' and 'b' under a rotor S pole are in the negative direction; and there is no current in bands 'c' and 'c̅'. All of the active conductors will experience the same magnitude of flux density from the rotor magnets; provided the current remains constant, there will be a constant torque exerted on the rotor for the whole of the 60° interval. There will also be a constant generated EMF.

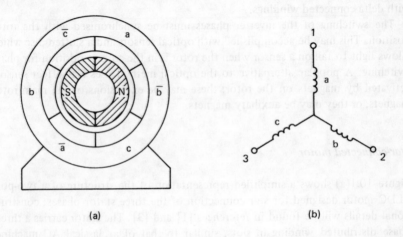

(a)

(b)

Figure 10.1 Star-connected brushless motor: (a) motor structure; (b) winding connections

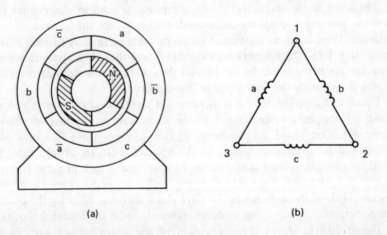

(a)

(b)

Figure 10.2 Delta-connected brushless motor: (a) motor structure; (b) winding connections

At the end of this $60°$ interval the rotor position sensor causes the bridge switching pattern to change, disconnecting line 1 and connecting line 3. This gives $i_c = -i_b$ and $i_a = 0$. The currents in phase bands 'b' and 'c' are now in the same direction, with no current in band 'a'; the relationship between the rotor magnets and the stator currents is the same as before. This sequence continues cyclically, so the motor develops an almost constant torque and generated EMF.

In practice the flux density under a rotor magnet will not be quite constant over the full $180°$ span of the magnet, and the currents will not switch instantaneously; the waveforms are trapezoidal rather than square. These departures from the ideal cause some unevenness, or ripple, in the torque and generated EMF.

Delta-connected motor

Figure 10.2(a) shows the structure of a two-pole BLDC motor designed for delta connection of the stator phases. The winding phase bands are the same as for star connection, but the rotor magnets span $120°$ instead of $180°$. Figure 10.2(b) shows the connection of the stator phases. For the rotor position shown in figure 10.2(a), current flows from line 1 to line 2, with no current in line 3.

Unlike the star-connected motor, current now flows in all three stator phases, with $i_c = i_a$. The relationship between i_a and i_b depends on the inductance and resistance of the windings as well as the generated EMF. Provided the currents remain constant throughout the $60°$ interval, the torque will also remain constant regardless of the relationship between the currents. To see why this is so, consider the phase bands 'a' and 'c' in figure 10.2(a). At the beginning of the $60°$ interval, the whole of band 'a' is covered by a rotor N pole, and band 'c' is in the interpolar gap. As the rotor moves, band 'a' is progressively uncovered by the magnet, while band 'c' is progressively covered; the fall in torque from band 'a' is compensated by a corresponding rise in the torque from band 'c'. This process continues until band 'c' is completely covered at the end of the $60°$ interval, leaving band 'a' in the interpolar gap. For the same reason, the generated EMF in phase 'b' is equal to the sum of the generated EMFs in phases 'a' and 'c'; if this were not so, the EMF difference would drive an unwanted circulating current round the delta. This equality of generated EMFs leads to near-equality of the currents in the phases [1].

The delta-connected BLDC motor has two advantages over the star-connected motor. First, all three phases carry current at all times, so there is better utilisation of the conductor material. Secondly, the reduced span of the rotor magnets gives a significant reduction in the volume of permanent-magnet material, with a corresponding cost saving when rare-earth magnets are used. For these reasons the delta-connected motor is the form which is most widely used.

Motor characteristics and control

We have seen that both forms of BLDC motor develop almost constant torque and EMF if the current and speed are constant. Since the basic mechanisms of torque and EMF production are the same as in the classical DC machine, it follows that eqns [2.10] and [2.11] also hold for the BLDC motor:

$$E_a = K_a \Phi \omega \qquad\qquad\qquad\qquad\qquad\qquad\qquad [2.10]$$

$$T = K_a \Phi I_a \qquad\qquad\qquad\qquad\qquad\qquad\qquad [2.11]$$

where E_a and I_a now represent the voltage and current at the input of the controller.

The speed of a BLDC motor can be controlled by varying the voltage applied to the controller, just as the speed of a classical DC motor is controlled by varying the armature voltage. It is not necessary, however, to use a separate circuit to generate a variable voltage. The same effect can be achieved by using pulse-width modulation (PWM) in the BLDC controller itself [1]. The technique is similar to that used in the PWM voltage-source inverter described in section 8.2; current control is readily incorporated in the same way. The result is a compact, efficient and reliable variable-speed drive system, with current control giving protection against overloads.

Permanent-magnet BLDC motors have two main disadvantages. First, permanent magnets cannot be turned off, so a BLDC motor will generate an EMF whenever the shaft rotates. A fault in the winding or the controller could then result in dangerously large currents if the motor continued to be driven by the mechanical system. The second disadvantage is related to the nature of semiconductor switches, which can pass current in only one direction. Mechanical commutators are inherently bidirectional, so reversal of the torque and direction of rotation is much easier with a classical DC motor.

10.3 Sinewave brushless DC drives

A sinewave brushless DC (BLDC) motor has an approximately sinusoidal distribution of current and flux density, as in the classical synchronous motor. The structure may be similar to that of a squarewave BLDC motor, with surface-mounted permanent magnets on the rotor. In this case the required sinusoidal distribution of flux density is achieved by tapering the thickness of the permanent magnets towards the edges of the poles. Alternatively, a wound-rotor construction may be used. The design of the stator winding follows normal AC machine practice to minimise the harmonic content (see section 4.8).

The controller for a sinewave BLDC motor is an inverter with a sinusoidal output current waveform; this will usually be a voltage-source PWM inverter (see section 8.2). Normally the phase of the inverter output current is locked to the rotor position, by controlling the inverter from a position transducer such as an encoder or a resolver. The frequency of the inverter output is then controlled by the rotor motion, as in the squarewave BLDC motor. The current phase is controlled so that the stator and rotor magnetic fields are at right angles, as in the classical DC motor and the vector controlled synchronous motor (section 8.5). If resistance is neglected, the phasor diagram for this condition may be deduced from figure 5.19 for the salient-pole synchronous machine; the result is shown in figure 10.3 which gives the voltage equation

$$V = E + jX_q I \tag{10.1}$$

where E is the EMF induced in the stator winding by the magnetised rotor. If ϕ is the rotor flux, then we may put

$$E = K_s \Phi \omega \tag{10.2}$$

where K_s is a constant for the stator winding. The torque is given by eqn [8.8], which becomes

$$T = \frac{3p}{\omega} EI = 3K_s \Phi I \tag{10.3}$$

When $T = 0$, eqn (10.3) gives $I = 0$; from eqn (10.1) the no-load speed is related to the stator voltage by the equation

$$V = E = K_s \Phi \omega \tag{10.4}$$

which is analogous to eqn [2.25] for a classical DC motor:

$$V_a = K_a \Phi \omega \tag{2.25}$$

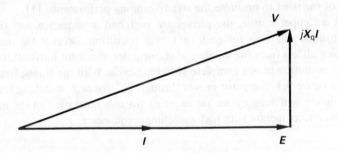

Figure 10.3   Phasor diagram for the sinewave brushless motor

Thus the no-load speed is proportional to the inverter output voltage. Equation (10.1) shows that the inverter output voltage must increase with load, even when the stator resistance is negligible; this is different from the behaviour of a classical DC motor or a squarewave BLDC motor.

Since the construction of a sinewave BLDC motor is based on the same principles as the classical synchronous motor, it has the same property of developing a smooth torque. It can also be produced in very large sizes, using a wound rotor with brushless excitation in place of the permanent magnets.

10.4 Switched reluctance drives

A switched-reluctance (SR) motor may be regarded as a variable-reluctance stepper motor in which the drive pulses are derived from the position of the rotor, as in a square-wave BLDC motor. There are two features which make this drive system very different from BLDC motors. First, the rotor of the SR motor contains no permanent magnets; this makes it inexpensive to manufacture, and totally passive. Secondly, the controller does not need to reverse the currents in the motor phases; this has significant advantages for the design of the electronic controller.

Switched reluctance motors

The structure of a typical SR motor is similar to the variable-reluctance stepper motor shown in figure 9.1, which has a four-pole rotor and a six-pole stator with three phases. Another common form has a six-pole rotor and an eight-pole stator with four phases. Normally the rotor and the stator are both laminated to reduce losses. The basic mechanism of torque production is the same as in the stepper motor, namely the alignment torque between opposing salient poles; but the stator and rotor shapes differ in detail from those of a stepper motor because of the need to optimise the steady-running performance [1].

As in a stepper motor, the phases are switched in sequence and the rotor moves through one step for each switching transition. Because the number of rotor poles differs from the number of stator poles, the rotor moves through less than one revolution in one complete switching cycle. With the three-phase motor shown in figure 9.1, the rotor moves through 30° for each switching transition; four complete switching cycles are required for one revolution of the rotor. SR motors therefore operate with high switching frequencies.

Controllers

The controller for an SR motor is normally of the unipolar chopper type (see section 9.4), giving PWM control of the phase current. A suitable circuit using two transistors per phase is the stepper motor drive circuit shown in figure 9.5. As with the inverter circuits described in section 8.2, other controlled semiconductor switches such as MOSFETs or IGBTs could also be used. Other circuits are possible which use fewer components, including one transistor per phase when the number of phases is even [1]. The circuit of figure 9.5 requires the three motor phases to be isolated – they cannot be connected in star or delta. Although requiring six connections to the motor, it has the merit of allowing full protection against fault conditions [1].

The switching of the power circuits must be controlled by the rotor position, so that a phase is turned on when the rotor poles approach the corresponding stator poles. As with the BLDC motor, optical (slotted disc) or magnetic (Hall-effect) sensors may be used to determine the rotor position. The performance of the motor is greatly affected by the timing and duration of the current pulses; microprocessor control is commonly used in high-power drives [1].

Characteristics

Torque/speed characteristic

At low speeds the chopping action of the controller tends to maintain a constant current in each phase; this gives a constant motor torque, which is related to the magnitude of the current. This constant torque is maintained with increasing speed until the PWM duty cycle of the chopper reaches 100 per cent; this is the base speed of the motor. At higher speeds the current will fall, as with a slewing stepper motor (section 9.5); over a limited range of speeds it is possible to obtain a constant power characteristic, with torque inversely proportional to speed, by controlling the pulse duration and timing. At still higher speeds the torque varies inversely as the square of the speed. The precise form of the torque/speed characteristic depends on the motor and controller design; further information will be found in Miller [1]. Since most variable-speed drive applications require adjustable speed rather than adjustable torque, it is normal practice to include speed feedback control in an SR drive system.

Comparison with other drive systems

SR drives have features in common with several other drive systems. The simplicity and robustness of the motor invite comparison with induction-motor drives, but the switching of the stator currents resembles the action of BLDC drives. They differ fundamentally from classical reluctance motor drives (see section 8.3) where the phase currents are continuous and the speed is controlled by an external inverter without reference to the rotor.

In comparison with induction-motor drives, SR drives have the advantage of higher efficiency and higher output per unit volume [2]. But the pulsed nature of the stator currents gives rise to torque pulsation, particularly at low speeds, and acoustic noise which can be troublesome at high torques [1]. The electronic controller circuits are simpler than the inverters used with AC and BLDC drives [1].

SR drives have lower efficiency and output per unit volume than BLDC drives using high-energy permanent magnets. But they have the advantage of a simple construction which is robust and inexpensive. The absence of permanent magnets confers two benefits: the motor can operate at a higher temperature, and the generated EMF is negligible if the stator is not energised.

References

1   T. J. E. Miller, *Brushless Permanent-Magnet and Reluctance Motor Drives* (Oxford University Press, 1989).

2   M. R. Harris and T. J. E. Miller, 'Comparison of design and performance parameters in switched reluctance and induction motors', *Fourth International Conference on Electrical Machines and Drives, IEE Conference Publication No. 310* (1989), pp. 303-7.

3   T. Kenjo and S. Nagamori, *Permanent-Magnet and Brushless DC Motors* (Oxford University Press, 1985).

Appendix: Airgap Field Components and the Maxwell Stress

Figure A.1 shows an idealised machine structure. The stator and rotor surfaces are smooth; the permeability of the iron is assumed to be infinite; and the windings are represented by 'current sheets' of negligible thickness on the stator and rotor surfaces. Current flows in the axial direction, perpendicular to the plane of the paper. Let the stator linear current density be

$$K_1 = -K_{1m} \sin \theta \qquad (A.1)$$

The radial and circumferential components of the magnetic field may be found by applying Ampère's circuital law to selected paths. The radial component H_{1r} may be evaluated from a path such as PQRS (figure A.1), as was done in section 4.2; from eqns (4.9) to (4.11), the result is

$$H_{1r} = \frac{r_1}{g} K_{1m} \cos \theta \qquad (A.2)$$

where r_1 is the radius of the stator current sheet and g is the radial length of the airgap; it is assumed that H_{1r} is constant along a radial path such as PQ.

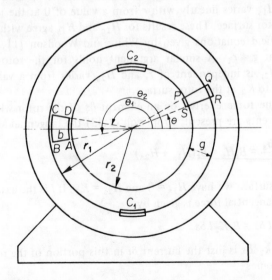

Figure A.1

237

Next we show that there must be a tangential component of magnetic field. Consider a path in the airgap which links no current, such as ABCD in figure A.1. We have

$$0 = \oint H_1 \cdot ds = \int_B^C H_{1s} \, ds + \int_D^A H_{1s} \, ds + \frac{b}{g} r_1 K_{1m}(\cos \theta_2 - \cos \theta_1) \quad (A.3)$$

where $AB = CD = b$. Equation (A.3) shows that there must be a tangential component H_{1s} along BC or AD. To evaluate this component, consider the boundary conditions at the stator and rotor surfaces. Take closed contours C_1 and C_2 enclosing lengths δs_1 and δs_2 of the respective surfaces; let the ends of the contours shrink to zero in such a way that one curved side is just in the iron, while the other curved side is just in the air. For the contour C_1, the current enclosed is $K_1 \, \delta s_1$, and Ampère's circuital law gives

$$K_1 \, \delta s_1 = \oint_{C_1} H_1 \cdot ds = H_{1s} \, \delta s_1 \qquad (A.4)$$

Thus $H_{1s} = K_1$ on the airgap side of the stator surface. Since we are considering the field due to stator current alone, the contour C_2 encloses no current, and we have

$$0 = \oint_{C_2} H_1 \cdot ds = H_{1s} \, \delta s_2 \qquad (A.5)$$

Thus $H_{1s} = 0$ on the airgap side of the rotor surface. If H_{1r} is independent of r, and the airgap length g is small in comparison with the radius r_1, it is readily shown that H_{1s} varies linearly with r from a value of 0 at the rotor surface to K_1 at the stator surface. These results for H_{1r} and H_{1s} agree with the exact solution of the field equations given by White and Woodson [1], subject to the condition that $g \ll r_1$. A similar argument holds for the rotor field H_2; the component H_{2r} is independent of r, and H_{2s} varies from a value of 0 at the stator surface to K_2 at the rotor surface.

Consider the force exerted on an element δs of the rotor when both stator and rotor currents are present. From eqn (1.43) the tangential Maxwell stress is

$$t_s = \frac{B_r B_s}{\mu_0} = B_r H_s = B_r(H_{1s} + H_{2s}) \qquad (A.6)$$

At the rotor surface we have $H_{1s} = 0$ and $H_{2s} = K_2$. If l is the axial length of the element, the tangential force is given by

$$\delta F_s = t_s l \, \delta s = B_r K_2 l \, \delta s \qquad (A.7)$$

The quantity $k_2 \, \delta s$ is just the current δi in this portion of the rotor surface, so eqn (A.7) becomes

$$\delta F_s = B_r l \, \delta i \qquad (A.8)$$

Equation (A.8) is equivalent to eqn (4.25), showing that the Maxwell stress calculation is equivalent to evaluating the force on a current element in a magnetic field.

Reference

1 D. C. White and H. H. Woodson, *Electromechanical Energy Conversion* (New York: Wiley, 1959).

Bibliography

The following lists are not exhaustive, and are intended as suggestions only.

Background reading

A. J. Compton, *Basic Electromagnetism and its Applications* (Wokingham: Van Nostrand Reinhold, 1986).

P. Hammond, *Electromagnetism for Engineers*, 3rd ed. (Oxford: Pergamon Press, 1986).

G. Stephenson, *Mathematical Methods for Science Students*, 2nd ed. (London: Longman, 1973).

G. Williams, *An Introduction to Electrical Circuit Theory* (London: Macmillan, 1973).

Further reading

D. A. Bradley, *Power Electronics* (Wokingham: Van Nostrand Reinhold, 1987).

A. E. Fitzgerald, C. Kingsley, Jr. and S. D. Umans, *Electric Machinery*, 4th ed. (New York: McGraw-Hill, 1983).

C. B. Gray, *Electrical Machines and Drive Systems* (Harlow: Longman, 1989).

P. Hammond, *Applied Electromagnetism* (Oxford: Pergamon Press, 1971).

J. Hindmarsh, *Electrical Machines and Drives: Worked Examples*, 2nd ed. (Oxford: Pergamon Press, 1982).

J. Hindmarsh, *Electrical Machines and their Applications*, 4th ed. (Oxford: Pergamon Press, 1984).

C. W. Lander, *Power Electronics*, 2nd ed. (New York: McGraw-Hill, 1987).

J. E. Parton, S. J. T. Owen and M. S. Raven, *Applied Electromagnetics*, 2nd ed. (London: Macmillan, 1984).

G. R. Slemon and A. Straughen, *Electric Machines* (Reading, Mass.: Addison-Wesley, 1980).

Answers to Problems

Chapter 1

1.1. 2980 N.

1.3. The machine will not work.

1.4. Use Ampère's circuital law and the reciprocal property of mutual inductance.

1.5. 0.5 H; 7.76 A; 0.193 H; 1790 N.

1.6. $-\frac{1}{4}L_2 I_m^2 \sin 2\phi$.

1.7. $A = 1.14$; $B = 0.0052$; hysteresis loss 57 W; eddy current loss 13 W.

Chapter 2

2.1. 90.9 per cent; 1.08 Ω.

2.2. $T = \dfrac{KV^2}{(R + K\omega_r)^2}$

2.4. (a) 20 A; (b) 90 rad/s; (c) 20 A; (d) 10 A; (e) 95 rad/s; $\dfrac{d\omega}{dt} + 40\omega = 3800$.

Chapter 3

3.2. 1:3.

3.4. $v_1 i_1 = v_2 i_2$; $Z_1 = k^2/Z_2$; inductance of value $k^2 C$.

3.5. $R_c = 739\ \Omega$; $X_m = 193\ \Omega$; $R_e = 0.127\ \Omega$; $X_e = 0.139\ \Omega$; $n = 3.04$;
(a) 659.9 V; (b) 97.41 per cent; (c) 1.38 per cent.

3.6. (a) Excessive magnetising current will burn out the transformer.
(b) Very low magnetising current, eddy-current loss unchanged, hysteresis loss 0.233 times normal value.

242

Chapter 4

4.1. $F(0)$ is the displacement of the θ axis to give equal positive and negative areas.

4.4. $T = \frac{1}{2} K_m^2 \pi r^3 l A_1 \sin\{2(\omega - \omega_r)t + 2\alpha\}$.

Chapter 5

5.1. 36 kW; 500 V; 58.3 A; 0.857; 45 kW.

5.3. $f = \dfrac{1}{2\pi} \sqrt{\left(\dfrac{pT_0}{J \tan \delta_0}\right)}$.

5.4. By Lenz's law, the rotor oscillations will be damped.

Chapter 6

6.2. $T = \dfrac{mp}{\omega} \cdot X_m I^2 \cdot \dfrac{1}{sX_m/R_2' + R_2'/sX_m}$

6.5. Effective rotor resistance R_2'/s in the first case, $R_2'/(2 - s)$ in the second.

6.6. Two equivalent circuits in series, with element values halved.

Chapter 7

7.3. Single-phase power factor = 0.900; three-phase power factor = 0.955.

Chapter 8

8.4. Fundamental: 197 W; 5th harmonic: 38.9 W; 7th harmonic: 10.1 W.

Chapter 9

9.1. $B_e = B_m = \frac{1}{2}B_s$.

9.2. $b = (S_f - S_i)(T_i - T_L)/(T_i - T_f); a = b + S_i; k = (T_i - T_f)/(S_f - S_i) J$.

Index

244